HAPPY ACRES

AUGSBURG PUBLISHING HOUS

HAPPY ACRES

by

ERLING NICOLAI ROLFSRUD

Illustrated by

DOROTHY DIVERS

MINNEAPOLIS 15, MINNESOTA

HAPPY ACRES

LIBRARY OF CONGRESS CATALOG CARD NO. 56-11793

FOREWORD TO PARENTS

This book is primarily for families with children of elementary school age. *Happy Acres* is intended as a supplementary book for reading aloud at family devotions.

The Bible is the Word of God; therefore, no other book should ever take its place at the family altar. The author of *Happy Acres* suggests that your family does as the Johnsons at "Happy Acres" do—have every member of the family who can read take part in reading aloud from the Bible. Little ones delight in taking their turns with such reading of a verse; yes, the First Grader may find it hard going at times, even with a parent beside him to help with the big words—but the joy of sharing and belonging is his.

Such child participation may early help establish the habit of daily Bible reading. "Train up a child in the way he shall go; and when he is old he will not depart from it" (Prov. 22:6). Nor will the Word of God return void (Isa. 55:11).

It will be best to read only one chapter of *Happy Acres* each day. You will find that each chapter of the book exemplifies or teaches the meaning of a particular Bible verse. The verse may be quoted directly, or its meaning given in everyday speech.

Following each chapter is a memory verse—usually the key verse of that chapter. "Thy word have I laid up in my heart" (Ps. 119:11). After your children have memorized a number of verses, you can occasionally review such verses by playing adaptations of games such as the old "spell down."

Each chapter concludes with family discussion questions. You and your children may find answers to these questions in the Scripture references given. Your children can learn to find their way about the Bible by looking up these references; where there are several older children you might assign a different reference for each. Just how many of these questions and references you use will depend on the age of your children, and the size of the family.

Except where otherwise indicated, the King James version of the Bible has been quoted.

It has been said of the laymen in a congregation that we may lose them if we do not use them. We may well adapt this thinking to those who gather about the family altar. While certainly it is a place where the father should lead, he should not monopolize. If it is only Father who reads from the Bible, juvenile thoughts are more likely to stray than when the child shares in the Bible reading, in the discussions, and in prayer.

Where, but at the family altar, is a better place for a child to form the habit of free and spontaneous prayer? It may be well and good for the family to join in a memorized prayer—but where only such rote prayer is used

FOREWORD

there is the danger that it may become merely "repeated." We suggest that besides having the entire family join in a prayer such as "The Lord's Prayer," that Father first offer up his own petition, then Mother hers, and each of the children in turn.

Some of the most beautiful moments of a parent's life will be the hearing of these prayers by their little ones. Parents of smaller children will hear some unique petitions and some phrases never heard at "prayer meeting." There will be times when parents will have to exercise self-control to maintain sober faces. But these little ones who utter them—are not such "of the Kingdom of Heaven"?

Soli Deo Gloria.

ERLING NICOLAI ROLFSRUD

THE FOLKS AT HAPPY ACRES

The red arrow-shaped sign pointed up a little road which soon disappeared under the spreading branches of large trees. But above the tops of those trees peeped the red roofs of a house, a barn, and a silo.

The white letters on the sign read "Happy Acres Farm," and the name on the mail box close by was "Peter Johnson."

Each morning when Ed Nelson, the mail carrier, stopped at that mail box, one of the eight Johnsons would be there eagerly waiting. For there was always mail for the folks at Happy Acres.

Of course, there were newspapers and magazines and advertisements such as Ed delivered to other farmers on his route. But no other family received so many letters —friendly letters—as the Johnsons. There were letters for Mr. Peter Johnson. There were letters for Mrs. Peter Johnson. There were letters for the six young Johnsons— Stephen, Mark, and Paul, the three boys, and for Ann, Melissa, and little Beth, the three girls.

Many of the letters came from far-away lands, from

people the Johnsons had never even seen. Melissa—who was in the Second Grade at the little white school house a mile down the gravel road—told Ed that on Thursday evening, all the Johnsons would sit around the big round dining table and write letters. Paul and little Beth were still too young to know how to read and write, so Dad and Mom or Stephen or Mark would write letters for them. Then Paul and Beth would press their thumbs on the ink pad and sign their letters with thumb prints.

Writing letters—and getting them—was just a little of the fun at Happy Acres Farm. There were more than a hundred acres of fields and pasture, and a bit of woodland, on which the eight Johnsons could have fun.

Naturally, it wasn't all fun at Happy Acres because the Johnsons weren't a story-book family that lived happily ever after. They were real people, so they had to work together to earn a living, and they had troubles like everybody else. Some years the Johnsons didn't have good crops. One spring the baby chicks got the sniffles and only a few of them lived. Once Dad's prized cow stole into the dewy alfalfa early one morning and was dead from bloat before anyone found her. At Happy Acres, shoes and clothes and farm machinery would wear out, and nearly every day Dad would have to fix something—the tractor, the truck, or maybe just a broken hinge or a burned-out fuse or a coaster wagon wheel that had come off. So, if the Johnsons had kept counting their troubles instead of their blessings, they would have been a very grumpy, unhappy family.

Every day at Happy Acres, there was laughing and joking and joyful words and thank-yous, but every day, too, there was pretty sure to be some little Johnson squalling.

When two little Johnsons had what Dad called a "mis-understanding," there were cross words, and maybe tears, and perhaps some pouting and slapping. Sad to say, though this happened only once in a great while, one of the little Johnsons would do something he *knew* he wasn't supposed to do—and then Dad or Mom Johnson would take that naughty child to the basement or the barn and talk to him with one hand.

Every day at Happy Acres, the Johnsons would sit down together in the many-windowed living room. Each Johnson who could read would join with Dad as he read from his big Bible. Sometimes they would all read together; most times, they would each take turns, reading a verse. How proudly now did seven-year old Melissa, with Mark or Ann helping with the big words, read in her turn.

They would memorize a verse of Scripture together, and sometimes Dad would see how many verses they could remember. There could be a story from a Bible story book, or a chapter from some other book that taught the Christian way. After the eight Johnsons had prayed together, there was a deep and quiet together-happiness in their hearts.

Though one or more of the Johnsons might come to these family devotions with unkind thoughts, each one found, like Paul, that while they read and prayed together the "badness all snucked away." Any hard feelings there might be would melt away as each child and parent learned more about the sinless Son of God who was hurt so much and yet forgave.

CONTENTS

HAPPY ACRES

1

THE JOHNSONS PLANT POTATOES

It was Saturday and potato-planting time at Happy Acres farm. But not all the Johnsons were happy about planting potatoes.

"Work, work, work!" grumbled ten-year-old Mark. "Seems like all we ever do on Saturdays is work, work, work!"

"Yes," agreed Ann who was nine years old, "and Lucia Hackley told me, yesterday, that *they* are going to town this afternoon, and this evening *they* are going to the movies. But what do we do? Just work and work and work, sticking these squishy potatoes in the dirt!"

"Wouldn't be so bad if all you had to do was to sit on the tractor and plow. The way Stevie does. Just drive up and down the furrow!" Mark looked enviously at his twelve-year-old brother contentedly steering the orange-colored tractor toward the opposite end of the small potato field. Only a few days before, Mark had overheard Dad saying to a neighbor, "Yes, Stevie can handle that tractor right well. He's getting to be my right-hand man."

HAPPY ACRES

Mark emptied his pail of the potato cuttings. Then he started back to the barrel of potatoes he had helped Mom and Ann get ready for planting. "At least one eye to *each* piece of potato," Mom had cautioned several times because Mark hadn't kept his mind on his work. He had kept thinking about Steve out working with Dad, doing man's work like changing plow shares and fueling the tractor.

Now as Mark trudged toward the barrel, he muttered to himself, "Steve is the oldest in the family so he always gets to be the first one to do things around here. Sure wish *I* were the oldest!"

He was slowly filling his pail with cuttings when Dad appeared from the opposite end of the field where he had been planting. Dad quickly filled his two large buckets. Then he looked at Mark and asked, "Something the matter, Son?"

Dad was easy to talk with. You couldn't argue him into letting you have your own way, the way Lon Gardner boasted *he* could with *his* father. You just did not *argue* with Dad. But Dad was always ready to listen, and he was always fair.

So Mark told him, "Well, I just plain don't like to plant potatoes."

Dad smiled. "Know what Mom is fixing for us to eat as soon as we come in this noon? One of your favorite dishes."

Mark brightened. "Oh? Which?" Nobody ever called Mark a second time to a meal. He would rather eat than play baseball, and baseball was his favorite sport.

"French fries," said Dad.

Mark saw the twinkle in his father's brown eyes. Then

the corners of his own pouting mouth just naturally began to lift. He heard Dad saying, "There's a verse in the New Testament that we might remember today. It goes something like 'if any would not work, neither should he eat'" (II Thess. 3:10).

Mark had to grin in spite of himself. He knew what his father was thinking, and it was true, all right, because Mark could certainly stow away plenty of the potatoes that would grow from these cuttings he was planting now. Planting potatoes and growing them was work. And if you were going to eat—and who wasn't going to eat?—you had to work.

When Dad told what the Bible said in answer to a problem, that settled it for Mark and for any of the Johnsons because they knew that the Bible is God's Word.

MEMORY VERSE: *Thy word is a lamp unto my feet, and a light unto my path.* Psalm 119:105

FAMILY DISCUSSION

1. Why do all Christians, like the Johnsons, know that the Bible is different from all other books? (II Timothy 3:16; II Peter 1:21)

2. Many wicked men have tried to destroy the Word of God by gathering and burning Bibles and by punishing those who printed and distributed the Bible. But no man has ever been able to destroy the Bible because God Himself has promised that the Bible will always endure. You find such promises in: Isaiah 40:8; Matthew 5:18; I Peter 1:25.

3. Why should our family, like the Johnsons, settle our problems with the teachings of the Bible? (Psalm 19:8; John 5:39; Hebrews 4:12)

2

TROUBLE IN THE POTATO FIELD

Mark always felt good when a hard job was done, and he knew that he had done his share of the job. He knew that *he* would be eating his full share of next year's crop of potatoes, that was certain. But he kept wishing that he could have a try at Steve's way of helping with the potato planting.

Steve was now coming close to Mark and Dad as the tractor and plow neared the end of the furrow.

Several times, with his father beside him, Mark had driven the tractor while plowing. Driving straight down a furrow had been simple. It was turning the big tractor around at the end of the field that was harder to do. So Dad had showed him how to slow the tractor, and then it was much easier to turn around and get straight into the furrow again. Mark knew that he could manage the tractor now in the potato field.

He turned to his father. "Dad," he said, "I wish I could take Steve's place. Why can't *he* set potatoes for a while —and let me make a couple rounds with the plow?"

"Think you can keep those big wheels hugging the fur-

4

row tight—and not squashing the potatoes we've set?"

"Yes, Sir!" replied Mark. "I'll be extra special careful."

"Okay, Sir!" grinned Dad. Then he signaled Steve to stop the tractor. He shouted to his elder son, "Stevie, we're changing shifts. Mark will drive the tractor for a couple rounds, and you can set potatoes in his place."

It was plain for Mark and Dad to see that Stevie did not like getting down from the tractor and then go lugging the potato pail down the furrow. However, Mark soon forgot how his older brother felt as he joyfully shifted the tractor into gear and carefully drove ahead.

As he passed Ann, coming to get her pail filled again, she looked at him in surprise. He sat proudly on the tractor seat, his hands fast to the big steering wheel. Ann looked up at him and shouted, "Oh, you, you smarty! You get out of planting potatoes—all because you're a boy and can drive a tractor!"

Then while she dumped potato cuttings into her little pail, she thought of Lucia Hackley again and murmured, "*She* never has to help with work like this! *She* never get her hands in the dirt! *Her* mother paints her fingernails for her to make them look extra stylish."

Her pail full again, Ann hurried down the furrow. She could hear her seven-year-old sister Melissa laughing gleefully as she played with little Beth in the sandbox back of the house.

"Hmm," Ann grumbled, "and there's Melissa! *She* could be out here helping, but all she has to do is to play with Beth and Paul. But I'm the oldest girl so I'm always getting the worst jobs."

That evening, when the Johnsons opened their Bibles, Dad asked them all to read together the Thirteenth

Chapter of First Corinthians. If you will read that same chapter in your Bible now, you'll know why Ann and Mark and Stephen grinned rather foolishly at each other as they read certain verses.

MEMORY VERSE: *Love is patient and kind; love is not jealous or boastful.* I Corinthians 13:4 (RSV)

FAMILY DISCUSSION

1. What was the trouble with Mark, Stephen, and Ann? Which verse, then, do you think made them realize what was the matter with them?

2. Instead of envying people, what should the Christian do? (Proverbs 14:30 and 23:17; Romans 13:13; Galatians 5:26)

3. Can you think of people in the Bible who were envious of one another? (Cain toward Abel—Genesis 4:5; his brothers toward Joseph—Genesis 37:11; Haman against Mordecai—Esther 5:13. Others, Daniel 6:4; Matthew 27:18; Acts 13:45)

3

JOSEFA

There was no sleeping late Sunday mornings at Happy Acres. For at eight-thirty the Johnsons must be ready to start for the church three miles away.

Getting ready for church was something that started on Saturday evenings when Mark collected eight pairs of shoes and took them to the basement to clean and shine for Sunday wear. Polishing shoes had been Steve's job until a few months earlier when Dad assigned the job to the younger brother. Now Steve's part of getting ready for church was to quiz each of the children who had memory verses for Sunday school, and to stack the Sunday school books in order on the vestibule bench.

To Ann was given the duty of undressing Beth, putting the little sister in the tub and giving her knees the special scrubbing they needed before they were ready for Sunday. When the baby girl was dried and in her pajamas, Ann took her to Dad. Dad carried Beth to the old Grandpa rocker. Soon he was rocking her to sleep while he half-sang, half-mumbled a lullaby.

Melissa and Paul had no special Saturday evening duty

except to get their own knees scrubbed clean enough for Sunday.

On Sunday mornings, Mark and Steve were out in the barns with Dad, helping with the chores. Done with this work, they dashed to the house, washed up and got into their best clothes—before Melissa, at 8:25 o'clock, would bong three times on the big brass dinner gong a missionary friend in India had sent to the Johnsons. When that dinner gong sounded, every Johnson must be out of the house and into the car.

Then down the graveled road they drove to the white-spired church set among cedars and maple trees. Because Mom was organist, she entered through a rear door at the church, while Dad and the children joined other families greeting one another and filing into the church.

This particular Sunday was an extra special day for the Johnsons. For a missionary from Madagascar was preaching—and this missionary had come from the very mission station where Josefa lived.

Josefa was a young Malagasy—but the Johnsons felt that he belonged to *their* family. For three years, Dad had sent money—and clothes—to the mission station to take care of Josefa's needs while he was at the Bible school. Josefa was a Malagasy chief's son. He had run away from his father's village so that he could learn more about Jesus. When Josefa became a Christian, the chief and his whole family would have no more to do with him. So, when Dad learned about Josefa—in a letter from a missionary friend there—the Johnsons just decided they would adopt Josefa.

Only a month before, a missionary at the Bible school

8

had told Josefa about the family in America that had been providing his needs. Just a week ago the Johnsons had received their first letter from Josefa and in it was a snapshot of Josefa. Everyone at Happy Acres excitedly looked at that picture of a wavy-haired, brown-skinned, husky young man. Steve had exclaimed, "Look at those muscles, will you? He looks like he could bend a steel fence post!"

Now Dad led the family to the pew where the Johnsons liked best to sit—the pew closest to the organ. Mom had just begun to play softly as they sat down, and right after the steeple bell rang, she began the opening hymn, "From Greenland's Icy Mountains."

Then Pastor Dale and the missionary appeared. The missionary was old and gray-haired. When he stood in the pulpit to preach, Ann knew she had seen his picture in the missionary magazine at home. As he told about his work with the heathen people in Madagascar, she kept wondering about Josefa and whether she would ever see him. Well, maybe, she could be a missionary nurse and go to Madagascar—then she could meet Josefa!

When the service was over, Pastor Dale brought the missionary directly to the Johnsons and said, "Reverend Peterson, these are the Peter Johnsons you want to meet."

The old missionary's eyes glowed happily. "So you are Josefa's family!"

"Oh," exclaimed Dad eagerly, "you know Josefa?"

"Of course, I know Josefa. I have had him in my classes at the Bible school. Ever since he learned about you Johnsons, he has been so very happy. When he heard that I was going to America on furlough, he told me over and over again how he wished he could sneak into my trunk and go with me so he could see *his* family. His own parents, you know, will not see him any more."

Then Missionary Peterson took Dad's hand, and said, "Mr. Johnson—Josefa told me there is something you could give him that he would greatly prize. His own people will not have him. They have disowned him. He would be grateful if you would give him your name. He would be proud to be Josefa Johnson."

Suddenly, there were tears in Dad's eyes. His children had never seen him weep before. The tears sparkled in Mom's eyes, too—and first thing the Johnson children knew, both their parents were dabbing at their eyes with handkerchiefs.

But Dad smiled, too, as he answered the missionary, "We shall be proud to have another son in the Johnson family! Josefa is a son I have prayed much for!"

Missionary Peterson's voice was very gentle when he said, "We are 'all one in Christ Jesus!' [Gal. 3:28]. It doesn't matter whether we have white skin or black skin or brown skin when we love Jesus—then we are truly one family."

(NOTE: Generally, mission boards do not encourage a family or a church group to "adopt" a particular individual at a mission station. The adopted person may consider himself a little better than his fellows because of such special adoption. Also, when an adopted individual fails to meet expectations, the sponsor may feel his efforts wasted.)

MEMORY VERSE: *He hath made of one blood all nations of men for to dwell on the face of the earth, and hath*

JOSEFA

determined the times before appointed, and the bounds of their habitation. Acts 17:26

FAMILY DISCUSSION

1. In the sight of God, is there any difference between the black man or the white man? Is the soul of one any more precious than the soul of the other? (Acts 17:26; Malachi 2:10; Galatians 3:28)

2. What, more than anything else, will make people of different races to be true friends? (The love of Christ. See John 13:35; I John 1:7)

4

CLOTHES FOR JOSEFA

Soon Pastor Dale and Missionary Peterson left for the town church six miles away. During the Sunday school classes that followed, the Johnsons found their thoughts straying to Josefa, and when they had all piled into their car to go home, there was no stopping their excited talk about him.

Was Josefa really and truly their *brother*, Melissa wanted to know. Paul, who was nearly six, couldn't understand how a brown-skinned boy could be *his* brother. If Josefa ever came to America to visit them, Ann hoped he would wear more clothes than he had on in his picture. She would be very embarrassed to sit with him in church if all he wore was a pair of baggy white trousers.

Patiently, Dad explained to the little children that Josefa could never be a really truly blood brother like Stephen or Mark. But when Josefa was born again as a Christian, then he was, in his heart, like a brother to them all.

Uncivilized people, Dad said, did not have last names like Johnson or Smith or McDonald. But now that Josefa

12

was civilized and wanted to be like his white Christian friends, he wanted to have two names. Because the Johnson family had helped him, Josefa felt that they were the closest to being his family, and so he wanted *Johnson* for his own last name.

When Sunday dinner was over, Mom and Dad decided they would each write a letter to Josefa. Ann, Mark and Stephen each wanted to write a letter to Josefa, too—but first they must take care of their usual Sunday after-dinner chores: Steve was the dish-washer, Mark was the wiper, and Ann the "cleaner-upper" who put things in their right places. Melissa, Paul, and Beth each took an extra look at Josefa's picture on the kitchen bulletin board before they went upstairs for their Sunday afternoon naps.

The kitchen crew glanced quite often at Josefa's picture as they worked.

"Wouldn't it be something, though, if Josefa really did come to see us!" exclaimed Mark. "Wonder if he'd bring along one of those long hunting spears they kill tigers with."

"Of course not," said Steve. "I don't think they have tigers in Madagascar, anyway. Besides, if Josefa came to America it wouldn't be to hunt wild animals. It would be to go to school. He wants to be a Bible teacher, you know."

"Well," said Ann, "just so he wears decent clothes. I'm going to write and ask him his *size* so we can get some decent clothes to send to him."

By the time the three had the dishes stacked away, and the kitchen all slicked up, and were at the dining table with paper and pens, Mom and Dad were just finishing their letters. Ann felt all goose-pimply when Dad said, "Wouldn't it be wonderful if we could afford to *send* for Josefa some day? Then he could get some schooling here in America."

Mom's eyes were misty as she said softly, "But even though we may never see him on this earth, we can keep loving him and doing whatever we can to help him so that some day he can help his own people to come to Christ."

"Couldn't we send him a shirt and some socks and shoes—real soon?" asked Ann.

Dad chuckled. "Madagascar is a warm country, Ann. It never snows there. So Josefa doesn't need a shirt and socks as much as he would if he were here in North Dakota with us. But we'll see what we can do about getting him some *decent*-looking clothes, just the same."

"Well," persisted Ann, "I certainly wouldn't want a brother of mine to go around without decent clothes on!"

"Yes, Ann," Mom agreed, "Josefa will need clothes. We'll send him some, this next week. But let's not forget that what he especially needs is our love, our prayers. He must know that his Johnson family is with him, always, in spirit. Even though there are thousands of miles between us, Christ's love keeps us close together, for *we are all one in Christ.*"

Thoughtfully, Steve looked through the window upon the fields of young wheat, and he said, "Seems like—when I think of Josefa—and when we plan to do things for him—why, Jesus seems so close."

"Yes," Dad agreed, "Jesus is close by when we help Josefa. Remember that Jesus said that when we do good

14

CLOTHES FOR JOSEFA

to those who are in need, we have done good to Him"
(Matt. 25:40).

MEMORY VERSE: *Verily, I say unto you, Inasmuch as ye
have done it unto one of the least of these my brethren,
ye have done it unto me.* Matthew 25:40

FAMILY DISCUSSION

1. The Johnsons have been helping Josefa while he has
been in need. What parable did Jesus tell to show how we
should help those in need? (Luke 10:30-37)

2. Whose spirit and love must we have if we are really
going to love and care for those who are not able to care for
themselves? (Christ's—John 13:14; John 21:16; Galatians 6:2)

3. Who is to help? (Luke 12:48; Mark 14:8; I Peter 4:11)

5

THE DANDELION CROP

On Monday morning as Paul looked out he saw bright yellow blossoms over the lawn. He slipped out of the house, and picked a handful of these dandelions and brought them to his mother.

"Flowers for you, Mommie," he announced happily.

Ann caught sight of her brother's bouquet and cried, "Oh, those aren't *flowers*, Paulie! Those are dandelions! They're *weeds!*"

Paul looked at his fistful of blossoms. "But I—I think— they're pretty. So I wanted to give them to Mommie."

Mom smiled at him. "They *are* pretty, Son. We'll put them in a glass of water, and set them in the window right above the sink so I can see how pretty they are while I wash the breakfast dishes."

"But, Mom," objected Ann as she took her lunch box ready to start for school, "dandelions *are* weeds, aren't they?"

"Yes," agreed her mother, "dandelions are weeds—but only because they have a habit of growing where we don't want them to grow. In some lands where flowers don't grow easily, folks would be delighted to have a bouquet of golden dandelions. Dandelions *do* have a lovely gold color—but we just have so many of them, and they grow so easily, they are a nuisance."

Then Mom turned to Paul. "What makes this bouquet most beautiful for me is that my boy brought them to me because he loves me."

That afternoon when Ann and Mark had returned from school, and had finished their after-school snack, Mom handed each of them a dandelion digging tool. The two children groaned at the sight of these tools. "Oh, Mom, do we have to dig dandelions again this spring?"

"Seems we have a new dandelion crop again," Mom replied. "We can't let the dandelions get fluffy heads or they'll spread their seeds all over the yard, and we'll have more dandelions than grass."

The lawn around the Johnson house was no small city lot in size. Now as Mark and Ann went out to dig dandelions, they were sure their yard was the biggest one in the whole county.

"Mark," said Mom, "you will work in the front yard. Ann, you will work in the back yard." Both children knew why Mom said that—if they worked together, they would get to talking so much they'd forget to work. Also they might have a misunderstanding about who dug the most dandelions.

Mark dug at the first dandelions as though he would like to cut them to bits. "You pesty things!" he grumbled at them.

After he had dug for about half an hour, he had an idea. Why dig the whole dandelion root out of the ground? Surely, if he got the green top off, that would be enough. So, instead of digging, he just yanked and yanked —and the dandelions disappeared much faster from the front lawn.

Mom came out to see how things were going. "Mark," she asked, "aren't you *digging* the dandelions?"

"It goes faster to yank them—like this," said Mark as he jerked the leaves off a dandelion, leaving the stubborn root sticking in the ground.

Mom shook her head. "I'm sorry to tell you this, but dandelions will grow if you leave their roots in the ground. So—wherever you have just pulled the leaves off now, you'll soon find a new dandelion top growing— and we'll have the job to do all over again."

Ann came around the house to tell her mother, "Maybe dandelions have a lovely gold color, Mom, but I don't think they'll ever look beautiful to *me!*"

Mom chuckled. "I can understand that, Ann." Then she looked at the basket of dandelion plants Ann carried. "I'm glad to see you are getting the root and all. A poet once said, 'Whatever is worth doing at all, is worth doing well.' That certainly is true of weeding dandelions—if we don't get *all* of the dandelions—it will soon be spreading itself all over the yard. The Bible has something to say about digging dandelions, too."

"Oh?" Mark and Ann both looked at her in surprise.

"Yes. This afternoon your job is digging dandelions. A person's job is his business. And the Bible says we are *not to be slothful in business* [Rom. 12:11]. To be slothful means to be lazy or careless. In Proverbs, we are told, 'Go to the ant, thou sluggard: consider her ways and be wise: which having no guide, overseer, or ruler,

18

DANDELIONS

provideth her meat in the summer, and gathereth her food in the harvest' " (Prov. 6:6-8).

Mark, ashamed now, kept looking at the ground. His bright eyes caught sight of several ants, one following right after the other, always going in the same direction, up and down blades of grass, and over any obstacle in the way. He grinned good-naturedly at Mom. "There's some ants right here—for me—to consider. Those little fellows sure know where they're going. And I guess I know where I'd better get going—*digging* dandelions, not just yanking them."

MEMORY VERSE: *Never flag in zeal, be aglow with the Spirit, serve the Lord.* Romans 12:11 (RSV)

FAMILY DISCUSSION

1. Does God expect each one of us to work for a living? (Genesis 2:15; Proverbs 14:23; Ecclesiastes 9:10; Ephesians 4:28; II Thessalonians 3:12)

2. Can you think of people who have never worked for a living, perhaps very wealthy men and women who have inherited much money? No doubt Mother and Father have read about such men and women in the newspapers. Have these people been *happy?*

3. Whether we work for our living on a farm or in the city, *how* shall we do our work? (Diligently—Proverbs 10:45; 12:11. Honestly—Deuteronomy 25:15; Romans 12:17.)

6

WHO IS GOOD-LOOKING?

On Tuesday, Ann was the first to reach home after school. She dashed into the kitchen where Mom was taking a chocolate cake from the oven, and she cried, "Oh, Mom, do you know what? Lucia says Dad looks like a regular ol' scarecrow because he's so long and skinny! And she says *her* father is a *handsome* man, and that *our* Daddy isn't at all good-looking!"

"Well," said Mom, slowly, "Mr. Hackley *is* a handsome man. But as far as *I* am concerned, our Daddy is the nicest man in the whole wide world!"

Ann was disappointed. Wasn't even her mother going to stick up for Dad? "Why, Mom," she asked, "don't *you* think Dad is good-looking, either?"

"No," replied her mother with a warm smile, "I guess our Daddy just is not what most people would consider good-looking. But he surely looks *good* to *me!*"

Truly, Mr. Peter Johnson was not a handsome man. He was the skinniest man in the Pleasant Valley neighborhood. He had a long, thin nose that humped out front like an eagle's beak. His ears were extra large, and his

GOOD-LOOKING

Adam's apple was like a great big lump in his scrawny neck. Only a few black hairs straggled over the top of his head; but Dad always said he didn't mind losing most of his hair because the less there was of it, the easier it was to wash and comb it.

Even when Dad dressed in his best clothes—and he dressed very neatly—he still wasn't handsome, Ann had to admit. And it hurt her to have her schoolmates poke fun at her father's appearance.

Mom understood how she felt. "You love Dad, though —even if he isn't a handsome man?"

"Oh, yes! I don't care if Lucia does think he looks like a scarecrow. I don't care if his ears are too big! He's my Daddy, and I wouldn't trade him for any other Daddy in the world!"

Mom's eyes glowed. "Even when your father was courting me, there were some girls who teased me about how skinny he was, and how he wasn't much for looks, and all that. But I didn't care so much about what he looked like to others because I loved *him*. I loved him for the kind of man he was—in his heart. You know, when we first see a person we just naturally judge that person by his looks. But when we really get to know a person, we don't pay so much attention to the color of his hair or what kind of clothes he wears—we know him for what he really *is*.

"That's the way with the Lord. He knows us for what we really are. He knows our hearts [Luke 16:15]. Remember the story in the Old Testament about the prophet Samuel going out to anoint one of the sons of Jesse to be king over Israel? The first son that Samuel saw was Eliab. Eliab was so good-looking that Samuel was sure

21

that this must be the one that would be king. But the Lord said to Samuel that he shouldn't just look at Eliab's handsome appearance, for the Lord didn't choose a man the way another man might. The Lord looked at what a man was like within, He looked at a man's heart. And the Lord looked at Eliab's heart, and knew that though Eliab was good-looking outside, his heart was not good, and so the Lord did not choose him to be king over Israel" (I Sam. 16:7).

Ann was thoughtful for a moment. Then she said, "It doesn't hurt any more—what Lucia said about Dad."

"No," answered Mom, tenderly, "when the Lord looks into Dad's heart, he finds a heart that is good—a heart that is good because Dad loves the Lord."

MEMORY VERSE: *Do not judge by appearances, but judge with right judgment.* John 7:24

FAMILY DISCUSSION

1. If a family comes to our house or to our church, poorly dressed and driving an old car, do we pay as much respect to them as we do to a family that comes richly-dressed and driving an expensive car? How are we judging people— Lucia's way or God's way? Read James 2:1-5.

2. Surely, the Lord does not want us to be careless or slovenly about our appearance. But it is when we become *vain* and spend too much time on what we wear—in order to outshine others—that we do wrong. Read I Timothy 2:9-10. Instead of primping and fussing over ourselves to make ourselves look better than others, what should we do if we are Christians?

7

EGGS FOR MARKET

Each afternoon Mark brought two large baskets of eggs from the poultry house and set them on a counter in the cool basement. Here, Ann would take the eggs from the baskets and sort the eggs according to size. She could usually tell just by looking at an egg whether it was small, medium, or large. If she wasn't sure, she set the egg on a little egg scale to measure it.

Ann put the little eggs in a case marked "Small," the middle-sized eggs in one marked "Medium," and the large ones in a third case. Not all the eggs were glossy white, though, so they could be put directly into the cases. Some were soiled. A few might be cracked. These cracked ones Ann would put in a separate carton for Mom who would use such eggs for cooking and baking.

Ann cleaned the soiled eggs with a piece of sandpaper or emery cloth. It was this cleaning of the eggs that Ann did not like. What she did like about her egg job was the money she earned. Mom and Dad paid Mark a share of the egg money because he took care of the hens, and they paid Ann a share for her cleaning and grading of the eggs.

Once Ann had been careless about cleaning the eggs. To her surprise, she discovered that the people at the egg market had counted the number of soiled eggs in the Johnson egg cases. Mom showed her the egg check, and pointed out that they had been paid less money for the eggs that were soiled. After that, Ann was more diligent about her business (Prov. 22:29).

This day as she sat cleaning eggs, Mom and Melissa came down into the basement. Melissa asked her mother, "Why does Ann have to clean all the eggs?"

"The eggs must be clean if we are going to sell them. *You* wouldn't want to use eggs that are dirty, would you?"

"No."

"Well, neither do the people who are going to buy and eat our eggs. So it is our business to take care of the eggs the same way we'd want farmers to take care of eggs if we were city people buying eggs at a grocery store" (Matt. 7:12).

"Do some people like small eggs better than big ones? Is that why Ann puts all the small eggs in one big box?"

"Not exactly. While I'm sure that children would enjoy the smallest eggs once in a while—that's not the reason for sorting eggs. You see, it wouldn't be fair to expect people to pay just as much for a small egg as they would pay for a large egg. So we sort the eggs so that people who want small eggs can buy small eggs, and the people who want to pay more can buy the larger eggs."

"But what if Ann stuck a few small eggs with the big eggs?"

24

EGGS FOR MARKET

"That would be cheating," interrupted Ann, "and I don't cheat!"

"Even if Ann happened to put small eggs with the big ones," said Mom, "the people who candle and pack the eggs in town would see that the small eggs were in the wrong box. And the man who buys our eggs would wonder if we did that on purpose, and then he wouldn't trust us, or care to buy from us. But, folks at the egg market like to buy our eggs because they know we try to be fair and honest."

MEMORY VERSE: *Whatever you wish that men would do to you, do so to them; for this is the law and the prophets.* Matthew 7:12 (RSV)

FAMILY DISCUSSION

1. Is Ann getting the eggs ready for market in a way that is according to God's Word? (Leviticus 19:35-36; Deuteronomy 25:13-16; Proverbs 11:1; Ezekiel 45:10; Romans 12:17)

2. If Ann were to put small eggs with the large eggs, would this be the same as lying or stealing? Consider what the Bible says about cheating: Leviticus 19:11; Psalm 101:7; Proverbs 12:22; 19:5; Revelation 21:8

3. Is it possible for a person NEVER to lie in any way? Can you say that you have never lied? (Jeremiah 17:9; Romans 3:23)

4. Who is the only One who has lived on earth without sinning by lying? (John 1:14; 14:6; 18:37)

5. What is the only way we can be made sinless in the sight of God? (Romans 3:24; I John 3:5; Galatians 3:13; Hebrews 9:28)

8

PAUL AND THE BROODY HEN

Paul stared. He was sure there was something moving inside the overturned box. It was the box on which Mark would stand when he reached for eggs in the highest row of nests. One board on the side of the box was broken off, and Paul could see that *something* had gotten inside that darkened box.

He watched for quite a while, not quite daring to get close and look right inside. Then suddenly a hen poked her head out, and looked at Paul as if to ask him what *he* was doing there in the poultry house.

The way she cluck-clucked to herself, Paul knew she was a "broody" hen. She wanted to set on eggs, but at Happy Acres Farm, hens were not allowed to hatch eggs because all the chicks were bought at the hatchery.

Now Paul watched the red hen go cluck-clucking as she went over to the water fountain for a drink. Paul decided, then, that he would peep inside the box to see if she might have a nest hidden there.

But just as Paul got down on his knees to look inside the box, the hen came flying straight at him, her wings fluffed out. Cluck-clucking angrily, she pecked him with her sharp bill.

"Ouch!" cried Paul, and he ran out of the poultry house and straight to Mom. Soon he was back with Mom to show the broody hen.

But by this time, the cluck-clucking hen was gone.

"She's very likely out in the yard, getting something to eat," said Mom. "We'll see if she has a nest under that box."

So Mom tipped the box up and there was a nest of eggs—eleven of them, closely-packed together. Mom felt of them and said, "Feel of the eggs, Paul."

"Oh, they're warm—warm like toast!"

"Yes. The hen must have been setting on them for some time. So we won't be able to use the eggs for cooking or to sell. Guess we might as well let her hatch the eggs." And then Mom said, "I think we'll let this hen and her chicks be Paul's chickens!"

Paul's eyes sparkled. "Oh, that would be fun!"

Mom turned the box back over the nest as the red hen returned to the poultry house. Spying Mom and Paul, the hen came running, her wings fluffed out, and she cluck-clucked angrily as Mom and Paul walked away from her nest.

"She's not a nice hen, though," decided Paul. "She could have better manners. She thinks she's smart—just like those big roosters."

Mom chuckled. "She is afraid we may be harming her eggs—she just wants to frighten us away from them."

Every day after that, Paul would run many times to the hen house to see his broody red hen. Dad pulled another board off the box so that Paul could see more easily inside without troubling the cluck-clucking hen.

One day as the hen came back to her nest after she had been out feeding, Paul was surprised to see her carefully turning over every egg with her bill. When she had finally settled herself down over the eggs, Paul ran to Mom to report what he had seen.

"Oh, yes," said Mom, "the hen must turn the eggs every day. Otherwise, the little baby chick that is growing inside the shell may stick to the side of the shell, and it wouldn't grow to be strong and healthy."

"That hen of mine must be extra bright," said Paul.

"I am quite sure it's just like every other hen, Paul, because all setting hens will do that to their eggs."

A few mornings later, Paul saw his hen out in the dewy grass. He watched her as she returned, with wet feet, to her nest. Alarmed, he ran to the house. "Mommie," he cried. "My hen has wet feet—and she's going right to her nest with those wet feet. She'll get the warm eggs wet!"

"Oh, that's perfectly all right, Paul. She's just doing what's best and right for her eggs. When eggs are hatching they need to get a little wet. In fact, at the hatcheries the hatchery men not only turn the eggs every day like the setting hens do, but they sprinkle the eggs with a little water, too."

"Did the hatchery men learn from the hens?"

"Yes, I'm sure that's where they learned."

"How did the hens learn?"

"Well, I'm afraid the hens never learned, at all. I'm sure your red hen doesn't know why she turns the eggs, and she doesn't go out and get her feet wet on purpose. She just does those things by instinct."

THE BROODY HEN

"What's instinct, Mom?"

"Birds and animals and fish can't think for themselves the way people can. When God first created us, He made us in His own image—that is, He made us so that we can think, and we can choose what we want to do. But birds and animals and fish were not created in God's image—they can't think for themselves. God gave them

instinct instead. Your hen has the instinct to hatch eggs —she does things that are right for her eggs even though she doesn't know *why* she does those things.

"Some day the baby chicks will break through the egg shells and come out—and they'll do many things that are best for them without knowing why. Little ducklings will go right into the water, but little chicks won't. You'll see your little chicks eating tiny pieces of grit and gravel, and they'll swallow that into their gizzards—they won't know why they eat grit, but they must have grit to grind up their food because they don't have any teeth."

"They do all that—by *instinct*, don't they, Mom?"

"That's right. By the instinct God gave them."

"I guess nobody—even if he lived to be a million years old—could ever know as much as God," decided Paul.

MEMORY VERSE: *O Lord, how manifold are thy works! in wisdom hast thou made them all: the earth is full of thy riches.* Psalm 104:24

FAMILY DISCUSSION

1. In your Bible you can find many verses to show how right Paul was when he said that nobody can ever know as much as God. (Psalm 104:24; Proverbs 3:19; I Samuel 2:3; Isaiah 40:28; Matthew 6:8; Romans 11:33; I Corinthians 3:20)

2. God created all things, and He understands how everything on earth lives and works. Does He know, too, everything each one of us does and says? (Job 31:4; 34:21; Psalm 94:11; 139:1-4; 147:5; Proverbs 15:3; Jeremiah 23:24; Hebrews 4:13; I John 3:20)

3. When Jesus was here on earth, did He, too, know what other men did and thought even without their telling Him? (Matthew 12:25; 22:18; Mark 2:8; Luke 6:8; John 2:25; 4:1-42)

9

A CALAMITY FOR MARK

Mark took the long-handled dust mop and stomped up the stairs. Here he was, ten years old, and expected to do girls' work—dust-mop all the floors upstairs!

His sisters and Paul and Mom had gone to town. Mom was buying goods from which she would make house dresses for the girls and herself. And *he*, Mark Johnson, had been told to have the floors of the five bedrooms, the bathroom, the sewing room, and the hallway upstairs all dusted spic and span by the time *they* got back.

Steve had grinned at him when Mom had told Mark about dusting the floors. Remembering the teasing look in Steve's face now, Mark's lips tightened in a straight line. Then he tossed the dust-mop handle to his shoulder, like it was a gun, and stomped to the top of the stairs.

Suddenly, as he turned there was a splintering sound, then pieces of glass shattered behind him.

Mark turned, instantly. When he saw what had happened, he gasped and covered his mouth with both hands.

For a moment, he could not move. It was as though

he were frozen still. His anger was all gone, and now, though he was a boy ten years old, his eyes quickly filled with tears and he began to cry.

The long handle of the mop, hoisted over his shoulder, had slammed into Mom's treasured old lamp which hung from the hall ceiling. Once that lamp had been the pride and joy of Mom's grandmother. Then it had been a lamp with wicks and bowls filled with kerosene. The beautiful hand-painted roses on the bowls and shades and chimneys had been sparklingly new then.

Mom had been so delighted when she had brought the old lamp home, and had had it fixed with electric bulbs lighting the dainty chimneys.

Now, one of those chimneys lay in bits on the hall floor. It could never be put together again. You couldn't buy another chimney like it. In all the twelve rooms of the old farm house, there was not another thing that Mom prized as much as she did that old lamp.

Through the open window, Mark could hear the distant purr of the tractor from the field where Dad and Steve were planting corn. Mark wanted to run to Dad now, for somehow his father could always find some way to help a fellow in trouble.

But there was no time to run to Dad. There was just enough time to get the upstairs floors all clean before Mom returned. He had better see that he did as Mom had told him.

First, Mark carefully swept the broken glass into a dust pan. Then, not knowing just what to do with the pieces, he poured them upon an old magazine on a table in his own room.

He dusted and dusted and cleaned, sometimes with

his tears making it hard for him to see. The upstairs floors were all spic and span by the time Mom and the younger children, their arms full of packages, burst into the kitchen.

Mom took one look at Mark's red-rimmed eyes and asked, "What's the matter, Son?"

Mark felt about as big as Paul, and burst into tears again. He threw his arms around Mom and sobbed, "I— broke—a chimney—on your Grandmother lamp—with the mop handle—and—I'm sorry. I know it was—your favorite—"

He could say no more.

Mom held him tight, patted his head. Then she said quietly, "It *is* my favorite lamp, Son. I love it because it was my Grandmother's lamp. I used to see it when I was a little girl, and I thought it was the beautifullest lamp in all the world. Grandmother knew that, and that's why she saved it for me.

"But even though I do treasure it—a lamp is just a thing. Things made of glass and wood can't last always and always. The treasures of the Spirit are far more important than the treasures that moth and rust can destroy" (Matt. 6:19).

Mom was quiet for a while. Mark stopped his crying. The girls went upstairs with their packages—once they had found out what Mark had done. Paul went out to the sandpile.

Then Mark said, "I knew you'd forgive me, Mom. But I just wish—I could do something—to make it up to you—for the broken chimney."

Mom smiled. "Yes, that's the way Christians feel toward God when we have accepted Christ as our Savior.

We want to do something—to make it up to Him. That's why we want to help with His Kingdom work—because He's forgiven us so much. So much more than just a broken lamp chimney.

"There's no forgiveness as great as the Lord's, no love as boundless as His for He gave His own Son to die for us so that we might be forgiven [John 3:16]. And the Bible tells us, too, Mark, 'And be ye kind one to another, tenderhearted, forgiving one another, even as God for Christ's sake hath forgiven you'" (Eph. 4:32).

MEMORY VERSE: *For God so loved the world that he gave his only begotten Son, that whosoever believeth in him should not perish, but have everlasting life.* John 3:16

FAMILY DISCUSSION

1. If some one hurts us or does evil against us, how should we behave toward such a person if we are Christian? (Luke 17:4; Colossians 3:13; Mark 11:25)

2. Will the Lord forgive us our trespasses if we do not forgive those who do wrong against us? Why? (Matthew 6:14; Luke 11:4; I John 1:9)

10

ANN DECIDES TO ADOPT
A GRANDFATHER

On Mother's Day, Mom and Dad each wore a white carnation. The young Johnsons each wore a bright red one. The blossoms had been cut from the potted carnations Mom grew in the sunny bay window of the dining room.

Dad proudly declared that Mom had a "green thumb" because she managed to have some house plants blooming all the time. Almost every Sunday she would have a fresh bloom to wear on her dress. Mom would always say, "Plants are like people—they do best when they are given loving care."

As they drove to church now, Paul asked, "Mom, why do you and Dad have white carnations—and the rest of us have red ones? Is it because you like white ones better than red ones?"

"No, Paul," Mom replied, "we don't wear white ones because we like them better than the red. We like both the red ones and the white ones. Carnations are worn on Mother's Day to honor our mothers. When people wear *red* carnations that's to show they are honoring mothers who are living. But Dad's mother, and my mother, are both dead—so we wear white carnations—because white carnations are for mothers that are not living."

"Oh," said Paul, "I'm sorry you don't have a Mommie."

Mom didn't answer, but her arm stole around him.

Then Dad spoke up. "Lots of times, Mother and I wish our mothers were living so we could visit them, and write letters to them. But we're glad though, that they were Christians and died in the Lord. Now they are with Him in the heavenly mansions" (John 14:2).

"Both our grandfathers are dead, too," said Melissa, sadly. "I can remember Grandpa Johnson a little—but I never even saw Mom's father. The Reynolds kids have lots of fun with their grandpa when he comes to visit them. Sure wish we had a grandpa like theirs."

Ann suddenly sat forward and fairly shouted, "I know what! Why can't we *adopt* a grandfather like we've adopted Josefa for a brother?"

Almost everyone turned and stared at Ann in astonishment.

"Adopt a grandfather! Whoever heard of such a thing as adopting a grandfather?" cried Mark. "You can adopt kids—and babies—but you can't go adopting old men, Ann."

"What's more," said Stephen, "we'd better make sure we can afford to keep Josefa in *decent* clothes before we go adopting a grandfather, too!"

But Ann's enthusiasm wasn't dampened. "Well, we wouldn't have to—really—adopt him. We could just sort of make believe he's our grandfather. We could go visit him. It would be fun to be able to *call* someone 'Grandpa'—even if it was just sort of play. And we could give him birthday presents, and Christmas gifts, and plan surprises for him."

"Say now," said Dad, "I think you've got a good idea, there, Ann. Maybe we *can* adopt a grandfather—that way. What do you think, Mother?"

Mom's eyes twinkled. "I think Ann has a splendid idea. I'm proud of her for thinking of it."

"But *who* could we adopt for a Grandpa," wondered Stephen who wasn't so sure Ann's idea would really work.

"Maybe," suggested Melissa, "the Reynolds grandpa could be our grandpa, too."

"Oh, no, the Reynolds kids would never stand for that," decided Mark. "They think he's so special they wouldn't want to share him with any other family."

Dad chuckled. "It might not be so easy to find a man that wants six Johnson kids yelling *Grandpa* at him!"

"Well, we're going to be real nice to our Grandpa," insisted Ann. "I'm sure there must be some old man—maybe a lonely old man that doesn't have any family—that would be glad to be our Grandpa."

"But *who?*" persisted Stephen.

"I think I'd rather have a Grandmom than a Grandpop," decided Paul.

All the Johnsons laughed at this. Then Dad said, "Well, we'll see what we can find. Perhaps it will be easier to find a Grandmom than a Grandpop. Guess we'll have to have our sixteen eyes open, and do plenty of thinking to get ourselves a grandparent."

The Johnsons all thought and thought the rest of the

37

way to church. But not one of them could think of an old man they could adopt for a grandfather or an old lady they could adopt for a grandmother.

It was just as they were slipping into their pew, that Ann got another idea. Quickly she whispered to Dad, "I've got an idea—where we can get a grandfather—"

Dad only smiled, put his fingers to his lips.

Ann knew that meant she must remember to be quiet. Dad always wanted them to be quiet and reverent in church; he always reminded them that if there was any whispering to be done in church, it should be done into the ear of the heavenly Father.

So Ann knew she would have to wait until after church, and after Sunday school, before she could tell where the Johnsons could get a Grandpa.

MEMORY VERSE: *In my Father's House are many mansions: if it were not so, I would have told you. I go to prepare a place for you.* John 14:2

FAMILY DISCUSSION

1. Do you think Ann has a good and sensible idea about adopting a grandfather? Why?

2. Can you think of any lonely old people in your church or in the neighborhood—who may not have relatives—and who would appreciate having us do such things for them as we'd do for our own grandparents?

3. What are our responsibilities to any old folks in our family? (I Timothy 5:8)

4. How should we treat all old folks? (With respect— Leviticus 19:32; I Timothy 5:1)

5. How does God want us to be toward our parents? (Exodus 20:12; Proverbs 1:8; 6:20; Ephesians 6:1; Colossians 3:20)

11

THE PLACE OF GRANDPAS

Ann could hardly wait until all the family was back in the car, ready to go home, so she could tell them the place to find a grandfather. Dad flashed a big smile at her as he slid behind the steering wheel and asked, "Well, Ann, where do we go to get a grandpa?"

"At Lund's Rest Home. In Woodbridge. They've got seven old men living there. We ought to be able to get one of them for a grandpa."

"Why not *seven* grandpas while you're getting one?" pestered Stephen.

"Nobody can have more than two grandpas," Melissa explained to her big brother. "You just couldn't have seven grandpas, Stevie!"

"Well, the way I see it, girls," insisted Stephen, "with this kind of grandpa, we might as well get set for seven —or seventy of them."

But Mom turned to Ann and said, "I think you've had two splendid ideas today. I'm sure those men at the Home must be lonely. I'm sorry to say that most of us never think about doing anything for them. We just

39

take it for granted that they are being well-fed and cared for—and, of course, we know the Lunds *do* take good care of them that way. But I'm sure those old men would appreciate it if some of us would give them some special attention—like taking them for a drive, or having them in our house for a meal and a cozy visit."

"You're right, Mother," said Dad. "What do you say to our driving over to Woodbridge—right this afternoon —and see what we can do about getting ourselves a grandpa at Lund's Rest Home?"

"We going to have seven Grandpas?" Paul wanted to know.

"We'll just see about getting one grandpa—this time," smiled Mom.

"How are we going to decide which of the seven old men is *our* grandpa, Ann," teased Stephen. "Maybe the one *we* want won't want *us*."

Ann had had enough of her brother's teasing. "We don't need to really adopt him, you know. All we'll do is treat him like a grandfather should be treated. Take him to our place for visits. Do kind things for him. After a while, maybe he'll like us well enough so he'll let us call him Grandpa."

Through Sunday dinner, and the kitchen chores after-wards, the Johnsons excitedly talked about how they would go about choosing one of the seven old men to try him out for a grandpa. It was decided, finally, that Dad would drive alone to Woodbridge—the town on the state highway ten miles to the south. He would see about bringing one or more of the old men back with him to Happy Acres Farm for a supper and visit. He would first ask Mrs. Lund which of the men had no relatives. He

40

would try to bring home the men who never got a chance to join in family fun and have supper at a real home.

When Dad had driven away, there were many plans to be made about this newest adventure—of adopting a grandfather. There was excited talk about which man Dad might bring home.

"I've seen some of those men sitting on the porch at the Rest Home," said Ann, "but I certainly never thought one of them would ever be my grandfather!"

"Like the old saying goes, Ann—don't count your chickens before they're hatched. We still don't know for sure if we'll be getting a grandpa out of this deal," Stephen pestered.

"I've seen all those seven men," said Mark, "when we visited with the Nichols family. A couple of them use canes. Some of them like to visit with the kids in the neighborhood. They tell them stories about old times. They're nice—all of them—except there's one guy there —he's got bristly hair that stands straight up. He's always shooing the kids off the place. Tom Nichols told me he's always scolding the kids because he says they make too much racket around the place. He's so grumpy that when Tom delivers papers at the Rest Home, that guy doesn't ever smile at him. He just sits there on a chair on the porch, sour as sauerkraut. Hope *he* has relatives. I sure wouldn't want Dad to bring *him* home for supper!"

"Yes," said Ann, "I guess I've heard Janie Nichols tell about him, too. She said he does a lot of walking around town all by himself. Once Janie's mother invited him to come to their church one Sunday morning, and he almost bit her head off."

But an hour later, when Dad drove into the yard, there

was only one old man in the car with him. Mark and Ann saw right away that it was the grumpy old fellow with bristly hair.

MEMORY VERSE: *You shall love your neighbor as yourself.* Matthew 22:39 (RSV)

FAMILY DISCUSSION

1. What are some reasons for an old man being grumpy?
2. If a man is grumpy, will it help him if we are grumpy toward him? If a man is grumpy, do you think he is a person who loves others a great deal, or is loved by others?
3. Are Mark and Ann glad to see this grumpy old man with bristly hair? Would you be glad to see such a man come calling? Is it Christian to want to be friends only with nice people, only with people who are kind toward us? (Matthew 5:46)
4. Read I Corinthians 13 again, and decide how the Johnsons—being a Christian family—will treat this stranger that has come to their house. (Also Ephesians 5:2; Leviticus 19:34; Deuteronomy 31:12)

12

OLD FELLOW WITH BRISTLY HAIR

"Grandpa Candidate No. 1 coming in," announced Stephen, while Ann and Mark drew their breaths in dismay. "A gay time will be had by all present! Ann, you got us into this. You should be the first one out to welcome Gramps!"

Ann flushed. For once she could think of no answer for Stephen. Mark started toward the back stairs, saying, "Excuse me, folks. I've got a good book I—"

Mom stopped him. "No, you don't, Mark. You will stay with us. While I go out to welcome our guest I want you three to read the verse on my slate."

Fastened to the cupboard wall above the sink was Mom's slate. She used it for jotting down things to buy in town and things she must not forget to do. Every day she would write on this big slate a verse of Scripture she would learn by heart as she worked in the kitchen. That is why Mark had once said about her, "Mom is just chock full of Bible verses."

Now the three young Johnsons read together Mom's

verse for the day: "Gather the people together, men, and women, and children, and the stranger that is within thy gates, that they may hear, and that they may learn, and fear the Lord your God, and observe to do all the words of this law" (Deut. 31:12). Mom had underlined the words "the stranger within thy gates."

The three faces sobered. Stephen said, "Leave it to Mom and her Bible verses to set us straight on things."

They could hear the parents and the old man—who had a squeaky sort of voice—coming into the house. So they dutifully walked in to meet their company.

"Mr. Haglund," said Mom, "these are our three oldest children."

Mr. Haglund squinted at Stephen, Mark and Ann as though they were not a pleasant sight. He grumbled, "Hm. Kids. Hm!"

Mom went on as though she hadn't noticed the old man's crossness. "Yes, and this is our oldest boy—Stephen."

Stephen nodded. As politely as he could, he said, "How do you do, Mr. Haglund."

"This is Mark." Mom smiled encouragingly into Mark's red face.

"How do you do, Mr. Haglund," said Mark. He was rather relieved that the old man hadn't offered his hand.

Ann had slipped behind her brothers. Now as her mother introduced her, she came out and did her best to smile at this man she was responsible for getting to their home.

Stephen offered to take his black felt hat. Mr. Haglund slowly handed it to him, then sputtered, "See that you don't squash it, boy."

Mom led the way into the cozy living room. Dad in-

44

vited Mr. Haglund to sit down in his own favorite chair —a big, leather-covered rocker.

"Nah," objected Mr. Haglund. "Too hard to get out of."

The comfortable rocker was only the first thing that did not suit this grumpy guest. There was too much sunlight shining on the sofa where he sat down, so Mom drew the drapes to shade him.

He made it plain that he did not care for any music. Not from the radio. Or record-player. Or "that pianner."

He did not want to look at any of the pictures or the magazines that Stephen brought him.

He did not want to see any of the curios from many lands which the Johnsons kept in the large china closet in the dining room.

If one of the children tried to speak to him, he acted as though he did not hear. Even Mom and Dad had a difficult time trying to visit with him. And when the three younger children came down from their afternoon nap and ran happily into the living room, Mr. Haglund just turned a peevish face in their direction.

Beth was too little to notice the old man's bad manners. She went up to him, put one chubby hand on his knee, then pointed to her white sandals and smiled. "See! New shoes; Me got—nice—new shoes!" He said nothing.

Ann wasn't sure, but she *thought* he didn't look *quite* as grumpy when Beth next patted his knee and said, "Hi!"

But Ann could hardly wait until Mr. Haglund left for the Rest Home after he pointed a finger at her and ordered, "You—Girlie—you get me a spittoon. Don't see none 'round here. I need something to *spit* in!"

45

Flabbergasted, Ann turned to her mother. No kind of tobacco was used in the Johnson home. Even friends who smoked seldom lit a cigarette or pipe in the fresh-smelling rooms of the old farmhouse. Once, in a hotel, Ann had seen a cuspidor. Curious to know what it was, she had looked inside it. Now this old man wanted such a vile-smelling thing in her own home!

Not knowing what to do, Ann hurried out to the kitchen. She was glad to hear her mother following her. Indignantly, Ann whispered, "Oh, Mom—a spittoon—we don't have—"

"I know," said Mom, quietly. Then she quickly opened a door under the sink, and reached for an empty shortening can. "Here, take this, Ann."

Red-faced, Ann returned to the living room and set the can down beside Mr. Haglund. He did not say "Thank you." He just rumbled in his throat and then spit.

Ann hurried back to the kitchen. She was glad to get away from the old man and to be able to help her mother with getting supper ready.

Supper that Sunday evening was one of the gloomiest meals the Johnsons had ever had. Though he seemed to enjoy eating it, the old man said nothing nice about Mom's supper. Mark wondered how anyone could be so glum about Mom's tasty cooking as he happily ate baked ham and baked potatoes.

Even little Beth seemed relieved when at last Mr. Haglund drove away with Dad.

"So long, Gramps!" exclaimed Stephen, more to himself than to anyone else, as he sank wearily onto a kitchen stool.

"You still want to adopt a grandpa, Ann?" Mark

wanted to know as he started out the back door with Mr. Haglund's tin can.

"Not *him,* anyway!" decided Ann. "Oh, I hope he doesn't *ever* come back here! Maybe we'd better look for a grandmother instead. I don't think we could possibly find an old *lady* that chews tobacco, anyway!"

Mrs. Johnson, however, had different ideas about the matter. "I know how you feel, children. Mr. Haglund certainly wasn't good company, and he's not a grandfatherly sort of person. He's a very unhappy person—and I think he's unhappy mostly because he doesn't have Jesus in his heart. So that's all the more reason we should invite him back. Perhaps we can bring him to Jesus!"

MEMORY VERSE: *He that winneth souls is wise.* Proverbs 11:30

FAMILY DISCUSSION

1. What is the easy and "natural" way for the Johnsons to feel toward this ungracious guest of theirs?

2. Which of them is showing the Christian way of treating Mr. Haglund?

3. Are each of us, even though we are not ministers or missionaries, to help win souls for Christ? (James 5:20)

4. Is Mr. Haglund the Johnson's *neighbor?* (Matthew 22: 37-39; I John 4:7-11; 3:18)

13

THE COOKIE GOBBLERS

The day after Mr. Haglund's visit, the Johnson children still found it hard to forget his grumpy ways. "Why," said Melissa, "I didn't hear him say *Thank you* —not once!"

"Every one of us tried to be nice to him, but do you suppose he could even *smile* at us?" asked Ann.

"Well, do you remember when Christ healed the ten lepers?" questioned Mom. "How many of those lepers— who had been so very sick and wretched and outcast— how many of them bothered to say Thank you to Jesus after He had entirely healed them?"

"Only one of them thanked Jesus," said Mark.

"That's right. And each of you may as well learn now that you are going to be disappointed in life if you expect folks to actually thank you every time you do something for them. Even though a lot of folks will appreciate what you do for them, not many of them will *say* so. Maybe they *intend* to say thank you, but they just never get around to it. So, it's a good idea not to *expect* to be thanked. And yet we should remember to thank others even though they may not thank us—that's part of the Golden Rule" (Matt. 7:12).

Mom pulled several tins of cookies from the oven. Six pairs of eyes lit with delight at the sight of those fresh-baked peanut-butter cookies.

"Those who would like a cookie form a line to my right," announced Mom.

In a twinkling, six young Johnsons stood in a row. Then, with Mark at the head, they marched up to a cookie tin, each one reaching for a cookie. As they happily munched cookies, they pranced around the big kitchen. The cookies eaten, Mark winked at his mother, then headed his sisters and brothers for the cookie tin again. When each had finished a second cookie, Mark headed his company back to the counter for a third time, but Mom shook her head. "One dozen cookies will take care of you until supper!"

"Say, I could eat a dozen all by myself—between now and supper," Mark told her.

For a few moments, Mom stood quietly watching the beaming faces of those who had enjoyed her cookies. Then she said, "I'm waiting!"

Six Johnsons looked at her, wonderingly.

"Waiting for what, Mom?"

"Waiting to hear just one cookie-gobbler say *Thank you.*"

Sheepishly, the children glanced at one another. Then there was a whole chorus of "Thank yous."

"Hm," said Mom, winking one eye, "seems like I heard some young folks around here finding fault with a certain old man because *he* didn't say *Thank you.* Reminds me of a verse in the Bible that says, 'Judge not that ye be not judged'" (Matt. 7:1).

Paul looked up at her, his freckled face puckered in thought. "Guess we aren't any better'n ol' Gramps—and he doen't have a Mommie to teach *him* to say 'Thank you.'"

MEMORY VERSE: *Judge not that ye be not judged.* Matthew 7:1

FAMILY DISCUSSION

1. What does the Bible say about finding fault with one another? (Matthew 7:3; Romans 2:1; 2:21)

2. Rather than find fault, what should we do? (Romans 14:13; James 4:12)

14

SECRET BROTHERS AND
SECRET SISTERS

There were more "Thank yous" said the next few days than Mom and Dad had ever heard before. None of the Johnson children wanted to be like the ungrateful lepers or the grumpy Mr. Haglund.

"It's been wonderful hearing so many 'Thank yous' around here," Mom told her family as they gathered together with their Bibles. "I hope we all keep doing it. It makes us feel good inside when we are thankful to others. And there's something else I wish we could try as a family. Let's all find the sixth chapter of Matthew, and read the third and fourth verses."

Ann was the first to find it. So she read aloud: " 'But when thou doest alms, let not thy left hand know what thy right hand doeth; that thine alms may be in secret: and thy Father which seeth in secret himself shall reward thee openly.' "

"But I don't understand how you can do something with your right hand without your left hand knowing," objected Mark.

51

"I know," said Dad, "that's really what we call a 'figure of speech.' What it really means is that we should keep our giving as secret as possible."

"What are *alms,* Dad?"

"Well, to give alms is to give food or clothing or help of some kind to a person who is in need. When we give this way—to other people—whether it is food or a kind deed—we do it quietly, without calling attention to ourselves doing it or to the ones to whom we are giving."

"That brings us to just what I want to tell about," said Mom. "The year I was at Teachers' College, I remember I had a 'Big Sister.' Each freshman student was assigned to an older student who was to be her 'Big Sister.' None of us 'Little Sisters' had any idea who our Big Sisters were for several months. All through the first half of the year, my Big Sister would be doing something kind for me—without my ever finding out who did it. Sometimes I'd find a little present waiting for me—and it would be signed 'Your Big Sister.' A couple times I overslept and didn't get my room tidied before I had to rush off to my first class—but somehow my Big Sister managed to get my room cleaned before the housemother came to check on the room.

"Finally, we had a party in our dormitory—"

"What's a dorm-tory, Mom?" asked Paul.

"A dormitory is a great big house where many schoolgirls or schoolboys live," explained Mom. Then she continued, "Well, at this party, we found out who our Big Sisters were, and when I met mine, I tried to tell her how much I had appreciated all the kind things she had done for me. She just laughed and said, 'Oh, I've had more fun doing it than you've had—you see, the Bible

52

is right about it's being more blessed to give than to receive'" (Acts 20:35).

Mom looked lovingly about at her family, then said, "I've been thinking—since Mr. Haglund was here—that maybe it would be lots of fun having secret sisters and secret brothers at our house. That way we could get special practice doing kind deeds in secret so that the person we do it for wouldn't even know whom to thank! Each one could plan little surprises for the secret sister or secret brother."

She paused, then asked, "How many want to be a secret sister or a secret brother?"

Dad raised both his hands up high. The children looked at him in surprise.

"But, Daddy," objected Melissa, "*you* couldn't be a secret brother to anybody. *You're* a daddy!"

Playfully, Dad shook his finger at Melissa and said, "But I can, too, be a secret brother, too!"

Melissa's hand shot up. "Then I want Daddy for *my* secret brother!"

In a second, all hands except Mom's were waving high. Then Mom said, "Tonight while you get into bed, I'll write each of your names on a slip of paper. I'll put the slips of paper into a cap, and when I come to say Goodnight to each one of you, you can each draw a name. And the name you draw will be the name of your secret sister or secret brother."

"Are Paul and Beth going to play, too?"

"Surely. I'll tell them the name each one draws."

"But if you don't have *your* name in the cap, you won't have any secret sister or secret brother."

"Oh, ho," said Daddy as he squeezed Mom's hand, "we can *all* be *her* secret sisters and brothers, then."

So that night, as the Johnsons snuggled into their beds, there was much happy planning of how each one would secretly do good to another.

MEMORY VERSE: *It is more blessed to give than to receive.* Acts 20:35

FAMILY DISCUSSION

1. Could we have fun playing the same secret sister and brother game in our family?

2. What rewards for giving in Christian love are promised in God's Word? (Proverbs 11:25; 22:9; Malachi 3:10; Luke 6:38)

3. What does the Bible say about being kind to one another? (Romans 12:10; Ephesians 4:32)

4. What people of the Old Testament showed special kindnesses to others? (Joseph—Genesis 50:21; Moses—Exodus 2:17; Boaz—Ruth 2:16; David—II Samuel 9:1)

5. What parable did Jesus tell about kindness to others, of doing alms for others? (Luke 10:34)

15

THE SECRET DO-GOODERS

The next few days were especially joyful at Happy Acres. Secret sisters and secret brothers were so busy thinking and doing happy surprises that there wasn't a grumpy word said.

Mark's part to keep weeded and hoed in the garden was the sweet corn. But when he went out on Wednesday afternoon to clean his corn, he found that it had already been weeded and hoed—and it had been raked so neatly with a garden rake there were no tell-tale footprints that might let him know who had done this secret good deed. Somehow, though, Mark was quite sure that Dad was *his* secret brother.

Ann found her room had been swept—but the dust and paper scraps were under her bed. So she was quite certain that Paul was *her* secret brother. Several times, lately, when Mom had been teaching him to sweep, he had found it took less time to just sweep the dirt under a bed than to get the dust pan and carry the trash down to the big trash box downstairs.

The same night when Ann slipped between the covers

of her bed, she found some sticky candy there. She giggled with delight, thinking about Paul.

One of Stephen's hobbies was collecting stamps. He found on his table a bunch of stamps and postmarks torn from envelopes. From the sticky fingerprints on the stamps and postmarks he was quite sure Melissa was *his* secret sister. Each night he found a cookie on his pillow. And whenever Melissa looked at him, she had such a broad smile for him that Stephen told his mother, "Melissa looks at me as though I am her private property!"

When Mom came home from church late Thursday afternoon, her eyes popped at what she saw in the kitchen. The four older Johnson children had decided they would be Mom's secret brothers and sisters as Dad had suggested. So Stephen had cleaned and waxed the kitchen floor. Mark and Ann had polished the counter tops. Mark now set the table while Ann was fixing her favorite supper—hot milk with cinnamon toast. Melissa had brought a large bouquet of wild flowers and had set them near Mom's plate.

As Mom, in her dress-up clothes, stepped into the kitchen from the dining room, Dad appeared in the rear entry. He had been out driving the manure spreader all afternoon. He had taken off his soiled boots before coming in now to get a change of clothes from the entry closet. Ann wrinkled her nose at him as he stood in the kitchen door, looking at Mom.

Mom glanced happily about. "Oh, bless your hearts! What a pleasant surprise." Then she looked around at each one and beamed, "Oh, you're so nice to come home to!"

"Me, too?" teased Dad, in his smelly clothes.

DO-GOODERS

"Oh yes, indeed, you too!" Mom cried. "I love my family so much it almost hurts. Only Christian families can be as wonderfully happy as ours. Truly, 'my cup runneth over'" (Psalm 23:5).

MEMORY VERSE: *Give, and it will be given to you; good measure, pressed down, shaken together, running over, will be put into your lap. For the measure you give will be the measure you get back.* Luke 6:38 (RSV)

FAMILY DISCUSSION

1. What is it that has made the Johnsons especially happy this week? (Giving, out of love—Luke 6:38)
2. What feeling that we have towards others will show that we are Christians? (Love—John 13:35; I John 4:20)
3. What is the second greatest commandment? (Mark 12:30)

16

THE STORY OF HAZEL MINER

Dad yawned as he woke from a Sunday afternoon nap in the hammock as the kitchen crew—Steve, Mark and Ann—came out on the porch and slumped into chairs and rockers nearby. Melissa left her dollhouse out under the trees, and joined them. It was an exceptionally warm spring day.

"What'll we do?" asked Mark.

"Too hot to play croquet. Or anything," decided Stephen.

"Dad, tell us a story about some really truly people," begged Melissa.

"Yeah, Dad, how about a story that happened in winter? Might help us cool off," suggested Mark.

"Well, I *do* know a story about a girl who once lived on a farm west of the Missouri river, out in Oliver County. And her story is a winter story.

"It happened long ago, in March, 1920. This girl, Hazel Miner, was at a country school like yours when a terrible blizzard hit. The snow came down so thick that Hazel wasn't able to see the school barn where her horse was sheltered. So she was very much relieved when her father came to help her and the younger brother and sister get home in their sled.

"Hazel's father first hitched her horse to the sled. He told her he would ride his own horse and lead the children's horse behind him.

"Then he went to get his own horse. He had tied it to a post nearby. It was just a little distance away, but the storm was so bad that the father right away disappeared from sight. Suddenly, there was an extra strong wind, and the children's horse got excited, and started out. Hazel couldn't stop the horse because it had only a halter on since Hazel's father had planned to lead it home. The horse went with the wind, and Hazel knew they must go *against* the wind in order to get home.

"In just a few minutes, Hazel realized that her father couldn't possibly find them in the storm.

"The horse stumbled into a slough, and there a tug unhooked. Hazel got out of the sled, and into the water. You see, blizzards often come right after a spell of warm weather—and this blizzard struck after several days when the weather had been so warm that a lot of the snow had melted. In order to get the tug hooked, Hazel had to wade up to her hips in water. Then she took the horse by the halter and led him to dry ground.

"Next thing the sled tipped over in a coulee. Hazel wasn't able to get it back upright. There was a canvas covering over the top of the sled. She ripped this right off and spread it on the ground in the shelter of the up-turned sled. Then she got her younger sister and brother to lie down on this piece of canvas. There were just a few blankets, and she covered them as well as she could. All the time her own wet clothes kept freezing stiff.

"It was soon dark. Hazel kept flapping her arms about herself to try to keep her blood circulating, and stay warm. She did not dare to lie down with the children for fear she might get drowsy. Besides, the blankets were just enough to keep the two younger ones warm.

"So, for hours, that night, Hazel walked back and forth beside the children. She sang to them, and told them all the stories she could think of, and she kept warning them not to let themselves fall asleep or they would never wake up.

"Finally, a terrible gust of wind tore the blankets right off the children. Hazel grabbed the blankets, and covered her sister and brother again. Very soon afterwards, the wind tore the blankets off again. So this next time, when Hazel had covered the children again, she lay down on top of them to keep the blankets from being blown off them.

"That was the way the neighbors found Hazel Miner the next day. She was dead, with her arms stretched protectingly around her little brother and sister—they were safe, and they are living today.

"Out on the courthouse grounds at Center, North Dakota, there's a monument to this unselfish girl. There's a Bible verse engraved on that monument. It is: 'Greater love hath no man than this, that a man lay down his life for his friends'" (John 15:13).

60

HAZEL MINER

MEMORY VERSE: *Greater love has no man than this, that a man lay down his life for his friends.* John 15:13 (RSV)

FAMILY DISCUSSION

1. Hazel Miner died while trying to protect her brother and sister. In a sense, is it possible to "lay down one's life" without actually dying for someone, or for some cause? (Matthew 16:25)

2. Think of people you know, or people that you have read about who gave up great possessions, or an important position, in order to be of Christian service.

17

TRIKE TROUBLE

Paul tugged his broken tricycle. to the back door. "Mom," he called, "my trike wheel broke. Please fix it."

Mom took one look at the broken wheel, and said, "I'm sorry, Paul, but I just can't fix that wheel for you."

"You *sure* you can't fix it, Mom?" It seemed to Paul that his mother had always been able to fix everything for him.

"No Paulie, I know I can't fix that wheel. It will have to be welded before you can use it again. I know who *can* fix it. Don't you?"

"Dad." Paul had watched his father weld broken farm tools.

"Yes," replied Mom, "when Dad comes home from the fields this afternoon, perhaps he'll find time to weld your trike wheel for you. I guess it is a good thing for boys with broken trikes that there are daddies that can weld."

"Yes, and some things Mommies can fix," said Paul. "Like teddy bears that come apart and let their insides out. And buttons that come off. And shoe laces that won't untie. But when I grow up I won't be a Mommie that fixes bears and buttons—I'll be a Daddy that can weld and fix tractors and trucks and plows and stuff like that."

Melissa had quietly joined Paul and Mom as they sat on the back stoop. Now she said, "And I'll be a Mommie that fixes bears and buttons. I'd rather do that than fix tractors and trucks."

"Well," said Mom, "the important thing is that we are happy doing whatever we are able to do. Some people are unhappy because they think too much about the things that they can't do, and not enough about the things that they *can* do. Mrs. Reynolds can paint beautiful pictures. I can't paint pictures at all. But then I *can* grow pretty flowers to make a beautiful picture in our bay window."

"Sharon Wheeler can play chords on her guitar," said Melissa, "and I can play chords on the piano. So we can chord together."

"And Freddie Wheeler can wiggle his ears, but he can't whistle like I can—because he lost his front teeth," concluded Paul.

MEMORY VERSE: *Now there are diversities of gifts, but the same Spirit.* I Corinthians 12:4

FAMILY DISCUSSION

1. Read Romans 12:4-8.

2. What different gifts or talents do the different members of our family have?

3. What are some talents that we may be able to use especially for the Lord's work?

4. Who gave each one of us our talents? (I Corinthians 4:7)

63

18

STEPHEN GETS THE JITTERS

The moment Stephen had dreaded now came. His Sunday school teacher, Mrs. Reynolds, turned to him and said, "Now, Steve, we want to have your report on Solomon's temple."

Stephen's knees wobbled as he stood up. His back was moist with perspiration. His throat felt dry. When he opened his mouth, the words he had planned to say just didn't come.

He glanced hastily at his notes. Then he tried again. He was careful not to look at the girls in the class, but talked instead in the direction of his best friend, Carl Storm.

Somehow, he managed, in a jumble of words, to tell something about Solomon's temple. Then, weakly, he sat down.

Later, he told his family as they drove homeward, "Say, was I all jitters! I'd rather do all the barn chores for a week than stand up in front of that class again!"

Dad chuckled. "Did anyone in your class bite you while you were giving the report?"

"Well, no."

"Anybody make faces at you? Pester you?"

"No."

"Well, Son, what should give you the jitters—just to stand and tell friends of yours what you learned from a Bible encyclopedia?"

"Well, they all look at you, for one thing."

"You wouldn't want them to be looking *away* from you, not paying attention to your report, would you?"

"No."

Dad laughed. So did Mom.

But Stephen could not understand why they should be amused. He had seen each of them stand up before people in church, at the schoolhouse, or other community gatherings—but neither of them ever got the jitters about talking to a crowd of people. Yet, even the mayor of Woodridge would stammer and get red in the face whenever he had to say something in front of many people.

"Dad," asked Stephen, "how come you're not nervous about getting up in front of people and speaking?"

"Hmm. I used to get plenty of the jitters. That is, until Someone showed me what was the matter with me."

"What was the matter?"

"I got the jitters because all the time I was standing up there trying to say something I wasn't thinking as much about what I was trying to say as I was thinking about *me*. I'd stand there, getting redder in the face by the minute, wondering what people were thinking about that skinny farmer standing up in front of them."

"And then—what took it away—the getting jittery?"

"It was the Lord Jesus that took away my fear. I learned that I can 'do all things'—even public speaking—'through

65

Christ which strengtheneth me' [Phil. 4:13]. When we learn to do all things as unto the Lord [Col. 3:17], we forget about me, myself and company. Then we lose fear, and don't get jittery. Fear, you know, doesn't come from the Lord. 'For God hath not given us the spirit of fear; but of power, and of love, and of a sound mind'" (II Tim. 1:7).

"But," said Stephen, "you couldn't—just learn to forget about yourself—all at once—could you?"

"No, indeed," replied Dad. "We lose our fleshly pride only as we grow in grace [II Peter 3:18]. And I learned that there wasn't anything that helped as much before I was to speak as to pray. God knows our every need—and if we ask His help—there just isn't any more powerful help that you can get."

Mom nodded her head. "Yes, Stevie, when you have to give another talk or report, remember, first of all, to do your part by preparing carefully what you are to say. Then, pray. And when you speak—keep in mind that it is your report, or your message, that is most important, not you."

MEMORY VERSE: *I can do all things through Christ which strengtheneth me.* Philippians 4:13

FAMILY DISCUSSION

1. Do *you* get nervous when you are going to take part in a church or school program? What is it that makes you nervous?

2. Does Jesus want us to be nervous when we speak in His honor at a Sunday school program? If we get nervous, are we thinking most about Jesus or most about ourselves?

3. What is the best thing for us to do before we speak for Jesus in front of people?

4. If we do not do all that we can in preparing our part in a program, do we have a right to expect the Lord to bless us in our part? (II Timothy 2:15)

19

MELISSA'S FIND

Melissa's light steps scampered up the walk to the house. She met her mother on the back stoop, and cried, "Look, Mom—look what I have!"

"Oh, a cocoon! Is it an empty one?"

"Oh, I don't know."

"Here. Let me see it." Mom took the cocoon still fastened to a twig which Melissa had broken from a bush. She felt carefully of the soft spun case and then said, "This one is alive—inside! We'll put it in the bay window, and one of these days we'll have a real surprise. You'd better keep your eye on this cocoon—or the surprise may get away from you."

And Melissa did watch the cocoon carefully. She would run to inspect it every hour or so. When she left for school the next morning, she took a last look at the cocoon and hoped the surprise would wait until she got back.

The surprise waited. Not until Saturday when the Johnsons were about to sit down to eat did Melissa see any difference in the cocoon. Now she noticed a tiny hole in one end—a hole that little by little was getting bigger and bigger. Excitedly, she called the family to see.

Carefully, Dad took the twig and cocoon and set it on the table where all could watch while they ate.

The hole slowly grew larger. Mark was the first to spy the head of a butterfly coming out of that hole.

Not a word was said as all the Johnsons watched the butterfly crawl out, then cling to the outside of the cocoon.

"See its wings?" asked Dad. "They are still damp. Just a little while now, and they'll dry. Then the butterfly will try its wings for the very first time."

Soon the wings began to flutter. Suddenly, the butterfly darted upward, then settled on a geranium in the bay window. Then it flew around and around while the children watched in glee. Soon after Mom opened the back door wide, the butterfly found its way outside.

"I once saw a butterfly carved on a gravestone," said Dad, "because centuries ago the butterfly was made a church symbol of the Resurrection. Hundreds of years ago when the first Christians would tell how Jesus rose from the dead, and how each of us who die in the Lord will likewise rise from the dead, they would sometimes explain this Resurrection by telling the story of the butterfly.

"First, you know, the beautiful butterfly is nothing but a plain little grub or larva. Then, when it has lived a short summer time, it spins its cocoon around itself and goes to sleep inside. If you were to open a cocoon in the winter time, you would find this little grub inside, and you would be sure it must be dead. But it isn't, even though it is frozen and doesn't move.

"Then, when spring comes, the sun warms the cocoon. The grub inside wakes up. It gnaws its way out of the cocoon—and comes out into the warm sunlight. Then it finds it isn't an ordinary grub anymore, but it is a beautiful butterfly!

"That's the way with us people. We people are plain and ordinary. When we have lived our short while on earth, we die. Then we are put in *our* cocoon—that's the grave. But on the great day of Resurrection, Christ will call us from the grave. We'll come out into the sunshine of His light, and we'll find that we don't have the plain, ordinary bodies we had before, but we have the glorious body of immortality.

"The body that will be ours in heaven will never get sick, or tired, or have any pain. And then we can see Jesus, our King and our Savior for ever and ever."

MEMORY VERSE: *I am the resurrection, and the life; he that believeth in me, though he were dead, yet shall he live.* John 11:25

FAMILY DISCUSSION

1. A butterfly lives only a summer season. Most people nowadays expect to live at least until they are seventy years old. In the sight of God, is seventy years a long time in which to live? (Psalm 103:15-16; Isaiah 40:6-7; I Peter 1:24)

2. Of what did God make the first man? (Genesis 2:7)

3. We say that our bodies are mortal because they do not last forever. What does the Bible have to say about our mortal bodies? (John 10:9; Psalm 89:48; Ecclesiastes 3:20; Hebrews 9:27)

4. We say our souls are immortal because they do not die. What does the Bible say about our souls? (Ecclesiastes 12:7; Matthew 10:28; John 5:25; 6:40; 11:25; I Corinthians 15:54)

20

NEWS ABOUT MR. HAGLUND

Dad looked up from reading the Woodbridge *Gazette* and told his family, "It says here that 'Mr. Hans Haglund left Tuesday for Minneapolis where he will seek medical treatment.'"

Mom nodded her head. "I didn't think that man was feeling well. I'm sure that's one reason for his grumpiness."

Stephen, Mark and Ann looked at one another. Though they said nothing, each knew what the other was thinking. They were not glad that old Mr. Haglund was sick, but they couldn't help feeling relieved that he would not be coming to their house for supper the next Sunday as Dad and Mom had been planning.

"I wonder what hospital Mr. Haglund will be going to. Does the paper say, Peter?" asked Mom.

Dad shook his head. "No. But I'm sure we can find out from the Lunds. You could call them."

"Poor man," said Mom. "I'm sure he's all alone. He must feel pretty lonely and blue. He could do with some cheerful words from some one."

71

She went to the telephone. In a few minutes she had the name and the address of Mr. Haglund's hospital. "I'm going to get a letter off to him in the morning mail,' she promised.

"Do you really like Mr. Haglund?" asked Melissa. "He was so grumpy—it's hard to like him."

"Yes, he's a grumpy man," admitted Mom, "and it isn't easy to like a person that is cross. I don't pretend that I'm writing to Mr. Haglund because I like him. Rather, I'm writing because I know that's what Jesus wants me to do. Jesus wants us to visit the sick [Matt. 25:36]. Right now, the only way I can visit Mr. Haglund is by writing him a letter. He is sick in his body. But he is also sick in his heart and soul. There's no better medicine for him than to find Jesus. We must each of us pray for Mr. Haglund."

Pray for Mr. Haglund! The Johnson youngsters looked at one another. They could think of many other nice people for whom they would rather pray!

Yet each one knew, from a heart that loved Jesus, that praying for Mr. Haglund was just what Jesus *wanted* them to do.

That evening as they sat together with their Bibles, and prayed, it seemed so very easy for Mom and Dad to remember the grumpy old man in their prayers. But the most that each of the young Johnsons could pray was, "Please, Lord, help Mr. Haglund."

As Ann crept into her comfortable bed that night, thoughts of the old man kept nagging at her. She shuddered at the memory of his saying to her, "You—Girlie—you get me a spittoon. Don't see none 'round here. I need something to *spit* in!"

72

MR. HAGLUND

Yet, Mom and Dad—and Jesus—would want her to pray for him.

Suddenly, the thought came over her that Jesus had loved Mr. Haglund, too—grumpy and bad-mannered as he was. Jesus had loved Mr. Haglund enough to die for *him* on the cross!

Meekly, then, Ann folded her hands and prayed for the cross old man. And each day, somehow, the more she prayed for him, the less grumpy she remembered him to be.

MEMORY VERSE: *I was naked and ye clothed me, I was sick and ye visited me, I was in prison and you came to me.* Matthew 25:36

FAMILY DISCUSSION

1. Mr. Haglund has never done anything for the Johnsons. The kindnesses have all been on their side. Why should they now pray for this man who has not even thanked them for their interest in him? (Matthew 5:44-48)

2. In the sight of God, are you and I any better than Mr. Haglund even though we may have better manners? (Romans 3:23)

21

THURSDAY EVENING AT
HAPPY ACRES

It was Thursday evening, and the Johnsons settled around the big round dining table to enjoy their "missionary hobby." Ever since Dad's best friend, Paul Clifford, had gone to India as a missionary, the Johnsons had realized more and more the many blessings *they* had at Happy Acres that the poor people in non-Christian lands did not have.

First of all, the Johnsons had the Gospel of Jesus Christ. They were never starved for the Bread of Life because they had their Bibles to read. Nor were they hungry for daily bread to eat. But there were thousands and thousands of people in heathen lands who were starving for food, and thousands and thousands who had never heard the Gospel preached.

The Johnsons were a healthy family, but even if one of them did get sick, there was a doctor and hospital close by. But great numbers of people in foreign lands had only witch doctors who could give them no real help.

THURSDAY EVENING

The Johnsons never suffered from the cold because they had warm clothes and a warm home. Many families in India and Africa and Madagascar had no homes at all. Such families hid in fear of enemies and from wild animals and from the terrible evil spirits and demons in which they believed.

So, because they had so many blessings, the family at Happy Acres Farm had decided to help—as much as they could—the missionaries who went to help those who were sick or hungry or in need of the Gospel. Many such missionaries went to faraway lands, some of them worked right in America. Mom would gather clothes the neighbors no longer needed, and the Johnsons would have a merry time packing boxes of clothing to send to those who needed clothing. One winter they had managed to send six big boxes of clothing away.

The Johnson children would collect old Christmas cards and birthday greetings. These they would send to a mission school in Zululand. There the mission teachers gave the brightly colored cards as prizes to the little children. Once, a teacher had sent the Johnsons a snapshot showing the dark-skinned youngsters happily holding the Christmas-card prizes.

Every week, as regularly as Thursday evening came, Mom would get out her missionary address book and the missionary magazines that listed the birthdays of faraway missionaries. Each of the Johnsons would help to write birthday greetings to those who would soon have a birthday. They would write letters to the missionaries and to native Christians who liked to get letters from the Johnsons. All of them had to have a part to write in the letter to Josefa.

They had finished writing letters to most of the missionaries when Mom said, "Now I think we should all write something to Mr. Haglund."

"But Mr. Haglund isn't a missionary," objected Mark.

"Oh, that is true enough," agreed Dad. "But—if you think it over—you'll find we write to several people who aren't really missionaries. Mostly, we've been writing these letters because we want to be of help to those who get these letters. Surely, Mr. Haglund needs any help that we may be able to give him."

Pen tops were chewed and fingered before Mark and Stephen could think of what to say in a cheer-up letter to "Gramps" Haglund. But Ann had no trouble getting started with her letter to the old man in the hospital. Somehow, the more she had prayed for him, the more friendly she felt toward Mr. Haglund.

MEMORY VERSE: *Declare his glory among the heathen, his wonders among all people.* Psalm 96:3

FAMILY DISCUSSION

1. Do you think that you can keep praying for a person, and not learn to like him?

2. What then, is the best thing for us to do, if we find we do not like somebody?

3. If we are Christians, we cannot be content just to know salvation for ourselves. We want to tell the good news about Christ to others. In so doing, we are following Christ's missionary mandate. (Matthew 24:14; 28:19; Mark 16:15; Luke 24:47)

4. How many missionaries can you name? What can you do to help the missionaries sent out by our church?

22

THE LADY WITH A BASKET

"Tell us a story about real people," Melissa begged of her father as he settled himself in his favorite chair.

Dad was tired. The day had been especially warm, and he had worked hard. He did not feel like telling a story. He felt more like just doing nothing. But his children gathered about him, hopefully, after hearing Melissa's plea.

"Well," said Dad, "I think I'll tell you about a lady with a basket. Some day we may go down to Minneapolis and I can show you a hospital there that this lady with a basket started many years ago.

"She was a nurse, a deaconess nurse. Her name was Elisabeth Fedde, but because she was a deaconess, people called her Sister Elisabeth. She came to New York from Norway—oh, about seventy years ago now—to help sick Norwegian sailors and immigrants there. She had no money of her own, and no salary. But she knew these sailors and immigrants needed her help, and she was sure it was God's will for her to come to help them.

"At first, Sister Elisabeth had no hospital where she

77

could bring her patients, and she took care of them wherever she found them. She found penniless and hungry immigrant people, hungry immigrant children without enough clothing. But she had a basket she carried on her arm, and she would go to the butchers and the bakers and the grocerymen and beg for food for the hungry people, and whatever food was given to her, Sister Elisabeth would put in her basket and take to the hungry ones. She would go to the housewives in Brooklyn and ask them for clothing they might no longer be needing, and she would put the old clothes in her basket and bring them to the little children who didn't have enough clothes.

"Soon Sister Elisabeth organized a relief society among the Norwegians in Brooklyn. This society helped her get

78

money and food and clothing for the immigrants and sailors who were in need.

"Sister Elisabeth started a Sunday school for immigrant children. She dreamed of a hospital where she could take care of her sick countrymen. She kept remembering God's promise that He would supply all her needs [Phil. 4:19]. So sure was Sister Elisabeth that the Lord wanted her to have a hospital that one day she brought sheeting and got her lady friends busy sewing pillow cases and bed sheets for the hospital—even before there was any such hospital planned.

"She hung a slate outside the door of the little apartment the society had rented for her. And any people who knew of someone that was sick or hungry and needed Sister Elisabeth to help, would write the name and the address of that person on Sister Elisabeth's slate. Then Elisabeth would find the sick or hungry person and care for him the best she could.

"Elisabeth's first hospital was just a rented house. But after a while the Norwegian people in Brooklyn built a big white hospital of their own. Sister Elisabeth was made the hospital superintendent, and what do you suppose one of her first jobs was?"

"I suppose she had to help operate on somebody," said Melissa.

"No! She had to go out and buy a horse!"

"A *horse?*" exclaimed Mark. "What would she want with a horse—at a hospital?"

"She needed a horse to pull the hospital ambulance. Back in those days, even the streetcars were pulled by horses.

"Well, Sister Elisabeth learned to do many things in

order to help people. Once, when she came to Minneapolis on a vacation, some Norwegian people there begged her to help them organize a hospital. So she did. That hospital was out in open country at first, with a lot of meadow around. So Sister Elisabeth even kept a cow to provide fresh milk for the hospital. The nurses would take turns milking that cow until Sister Elisabeth was able to hire a young Danish immigrant to take care of the cow. This man not only brushed the cow, but he *washed* her as well. Also he scrubbed the cow's stable and kept the floor sprinkled with saw dust.

"After years of hard work in her hospitals at Minneapolis and New York, Sister Elisabeth became very ill. She went back to Norway. She had to give up nursing, and then she married.

"But to the end of her long life, she was always called Sister Elisabeth because whenever there was someone sick or in need in her neighborhood, Elisabeth just could not stay at home, but had to go and help."

MEMORY VERSE: *Have no anxiety about anything, but in everything by prayer and supplication with thanksgiving let your requests be made known to God.* Philippians 4:6 (RSV)

FAMILY DISCUSSION

1. How was Elisabeth Fedde's life different from the life most of us live?

2. Read Luke 10:30-37. Sister Elisabeth was like which of these three men?

3. Can you think of a neighbor or friend who is like Sister Elisabeth, always ready to help those who are in need?

4. Read Luke 4:38-41 and 5:12-17.

23

STEPHEN IS WORRIED

It was time for Stephen to be in bed, but he still sat at the dining table, his school books spread before him. In a few days, he would be writing his eighth grade examinations. So Mom had been going through his history text with him, asking him questions.

Now Stephen ran his fingers nervously through his hair. "Boy, I sure hope I don't flunk that history test! Math doesn't bother me much. Or science. But history! I just get scared when I think about a history test. So many things to remember. Dates, names, places—"

"You *are* worried about it, aren't you, Son?"

"I surely am!"

"Then I think it would be a good idea to forget about this history book, and get your Bible instead. There's a verse in your Bible that I think will help you with your history examination."

Stephen looked at his mother, questioningly. She always had a Bible verse handy for setting a fellow straight. Usually, she would just say what the verse was. This time she wanted him to find it himself.

He fetched his Bible, then sat down with Mom again. "Okay, Mom, what's the good word this time?"

"Look in Paul's letter to the Philippians. Somewhere in the fourth chapter, and you'll read a verse that starts: 'In nothing be anxious.'"

Stephen ran his finger down the page, and stopped at the sixth verse in the fourth chapter. "Oh, yes. Here it is. 'In nothing be anxious; but in everything by prayer and supplication with thanksgiving let your requests be made known unto God.'"

Mom smiled. "You are nervous because you have been anxious about that test. There are thousands of people who get so nervous they get sick. Many of them have nervous breakdowns, and then spend months and years in hospitals—all because they have been *anxious* about too many things.

"But if we are Christians, and follow God's Word in our lives, we need be anxious about *nothing*. God wants us to let Him take care of anything that worries us" (I Peter 5:7).

Stephen was puzzled. "I can see that I should pray about this test. But *just* praying about this history test—and not studying for it—well, that wouldn't seem right."

"No," replied Mom, "that wouldn't be right. The Lord expects you to study. He expects you to do all you can to prepare sensibly for your test. But He does *not* want you to *worry*. Just worrying about something has never yet helped anybody. 'Which of you by being anxious can add one cubit to his stature?'" (Luke 12:25.)

"I think I get it now," said Stephen. "Stuff as much history as I can get into my head. But no use biting my nails, worrying."

82

STEPHEN WORRIES

MEMORY VERSE: *And which of you by being anxious can add one cubit to his span of life?* Luke 12:25 (RSV)

FAMILY DISCUSSION

1. When we worry about things, do we then have full faith in God? (Matthew 6:31-34)

2. Most of the troubles we worry about never happen to us. That makes it all the more foolish to worry. Instead of making matters worse by worrying, what should we do? Read Psalm 37:3-10. In this Psalm, what does God encourage us to do? What are the rewards He promises for *trusting* in Him? For *delighting* in Him? For committing, or giving, our way to His way? Not fretting? For ceasing our anger?

MOM INSPECTS

Mom gasped with surprise as she stepped into the girls' room. Not only were there paper scraps all over the floor, but the table and dresser tops and chairs were strewn with all the different things that can clutter young girls' rooms. What was worse, there on the floor were Ann's pajamas, and a dress belonging to Melissa.

The closet door stood open and showed dresses and sweaters plopped in a heap on the floor.

Paul followed his mother into the room. He saw the look on Mom's face and then he remarked, "They don't keep their room nice, do they?"

Mom shook her head. It was Saturday. Ann and Melissa had scampered happily off for a visit with two of their schoolmates who lived not far away. They had hurried away without first tidying their room.

"This is like the way Suky keeps *her* place," said Paul as he looked about the tousled room.

Mom laughed. Suky was a big brood sow. Her pen was a messy looking place what with her constant rooting and digging about the ground.

MOM INSPECTS

Mark happened by in time to hear Paul's remark. As Mom closed the door of the girls' room, Mark said to her as he stuck out his chest, "If you are out on an inspection tour, ma'am, just come this way!" He opened the door to the room he shared with Stephen.

That room was, Mom declared, "Trim as a barracks." Neither Mark nor Stephen had liked to make their beds or clean their room until a soldier cousin had come to visit and had told them how neatly soldiers had to keep their barracks.

As Mom left Mark's room, she thought she saw a spark of mischief in his eyes. She was not greatly surprised when she came upstairs an hour later and found a paper sign tacked to the door of the girls' room. In big bold letters the crayoned sign announced:

"SUKY LIVES HERE!"

Mom left the sign on the door. She was at work in her sewing room when Ann and Melissa came home and hurried up to their room. She heard Ann exclaim, "Say! Look! *Suky—lives here!* Why, the idea! I'd just like to know—say, I betcha Mark made that sign!"

"Why would he put that sign on our door?" asked Melissa.

Ann did not have time to answer before Mom joined them. "Hello, Girls," said Mom. "Did you have a nice time?"

"Oh, yes," chorused the two girls. Then Melissa asked, "Mom, why did Mark put that sign about Suky on our door?"

Mom eyed the messy room. "Well," she said, "I just wonder why!"

Ann, however, flushed. She wasn't wondering why.

"Suky is a big pig," said Melissa, "and we're girls—in this room."

"Yes, but I guess we let our room look like Suky's pen today," admitted Ann.

Mom went over to the little blue bookcase and got Ann's white Bible. She opened it to a certain page, and laid it on the table. She pointed to a verse that read: "Let all things be done decently and in order" (I Cor. 14:40).

Then she said, "This verse wasn't written especially for housekeepers. It was advice to some people in the church at Corinth who were very disorderly about the way they had church services. But it's good advice for housekeepers, too.

"Being neat and orderly is just plain common sense. You know that if you didn't keep your room in order, why, in a few days you'd be stumbling over things, and you wouldn't be able to find anything without stirring around in the mess. It's just much easier to live with people who do things 'decently and in order.'"

MEMORY VERSE: *Let all things be done decently and in order.* I Corinthians 14:40

FAMILY DISCUSSION

1. When we are untidy, are we also careless and slothful? Does carelessness bring waste? Consider Ecclesiastes 10:18.

2. Would it be showing respect to God if we let our church be untidy and shabby?

3. Turn to Luke 10:38-42 and you will read about a certain worried housekeeper. We are sure she must have done a neat job of taking care of her house, but what did Jesus consider more important than her house keeping? Which sister had chosen the "good part"?

25

THE QUIET GAME

Saturday had been a wearisome day for Mom. She had done an extra "small wash." She had ironed Sunday dresses for the girls. She had done some extra mending besides the usual chores about the house. Now as the family gathered about the supper table, it seemed that the children were all talking at once.

"You look tired, Molly," Dad said to her, tenderly.

"Yes," she answered, "I am tired. I hope I can have a nap tomorrow afternoon."

"We'll just see that you do," promised Dad.

The children settled noisily. As Dad bowed his head for grace, they were quickly still. As soon as he had finished the prayer, though, the chatter began again.

Dad held up his hand. That was his signal for all to be quiet. When the chatter paused, he announced, "We'll play the Quiet Game during supper."

If they did not play it too often, the Johnson children enjoyed the Quiet Game though they knew it was just a game their father had invented to stop them when they became too noisy. The object of the Quiet Game was to see who could keep from talking the longest. As soon as someone talked, he was out of the game.

Now everyone in the Johnson family joined in the Quiet Game. Silently, they passed the food around, and ate.

As usual, Mark was the first to want a second helping. Now he pointed to the bowl of mashed potatoes, then to his own plate. The potatoes were near Stephen. But he acted as though he could not understand what Mark wanted. So Mark went through all his motions again. Not until Dad nudged him, did Stephen pass the potatoes to his brother.

As more second helpings were wanted, there were more and more motions and signs. There were many smiles and grins resulting, but no one laughed aloud because if he did that would put him out of the game.

Not until time for dessert was a voice heard. Then, as Dad was making exaggerated motions to show Mom that he wanted only *half* a piece of lemon pie, Beth giggled and said, "You funny, Daddy!"

With supper done, Ann and Stephen had not yet said a word. So the game continued through the dishwashing while the other children merrily tried to trick them into talking.

Stephen won the game. Even by the time the family gathered for devotions, no one had succeeded in getting him to speak out loud.

"Game is over," announced Dad as they sat down. "Let's give the champion a big hand."

They all clapped until Dad held up his hand again for quiet. Then he said, "There's a 'time to keep silence, and a time to speak'" (Eccles. 3:7).

THE QUIET GAME

Mom looked at him gratefully. She had appreciated the quiet of the game.

MEMORY VERSE: *Be still, and know that I am God.* Psalm 46:10

FAMILY DISCUSSION

1. When is it easier to get cross with one another? When our house is noisy or quiet? (Proverbs 17:1)

2. Why are there Quiet signs on streets near hospitals? What is the best place for resting, or for gaining strength after illness? (Ecclesiastes 4:6; Proverbs 1:33; Isaiah 32:17)

3. Why should we be quiet in church? (Psalm 46:10)

26

ONE PEW FOR MELISSA

The Johnsons had nearly reached the church Sunday morning when Melissa said, "I want to sit with Patsy and Sharon and Kay in church today. They want me to."

Mom, from her place at the organ, had seen Melissa's three little friends sitting together in the balcony of the church several Sundays now. Each Sunday the girls had become noisier and whispered more and more during the service. Their parents who sat on the main floor knew nothing about how the three little girls were misbehaving.

Dad, who always sat with his six children in one of the front pews, had never seen the bad manners of the three girls. But he shook his head at Melissa and told her, "No, you will sit with your own family like always, Melissa."

Each of the older children had learned at one time or another that Dad would not give them permission to sit separately with friends. Though other boys and girls might be allowed to sit with groups of their friends wherever they liked in church, the Johnson youngsters knew there was only one place for them—and that was together, with Dad.

"We come to worship God in church, Melissa," said Dad gently. "We do not come to church to visit with our friends. If we are to heed the Word of God as the pastor preaches it to us, then we must be quiet or we will not have ears that hear. When we are in church we are in the temple of the Lord. What is it that the choir sings when we start the service?"

Stephen thought for a moment and then recited: "The Lord is in his holy temple: let all the earth keep silence before him" (Hab. 2:20).

"That's right. And another verse from the Bible that we should remember when we come to church is: 'Ye shall keep my sabbath, and reverence my sanctuary: I am the Lord'" (Lev. 19:30).

Melissa said no more about sitting with Patsy and Sharon and Kay. She settled herself in the pew with the other Johnsons, not really wanting to be where she was, yet knowing that she was where she *ought* to be. In the pew with Dad, there was no whispering. And you sat quietly. You heard what the preacher said, even though you might not *want* to be good.

It was while the pastor was praying that she heard loud whispering up in the balcony. Then Sharon's twittery giggle rippled out over the entire church.

Suddenly, Melissa was very glad she was there in the pew with Dad. It was much easier for a girl to be quiet in the Lord's temple when her own father was there beside her—quiet, and loving the holy stillness of the sanctuary of God.

91

MEMORY VERSE: *Ye shall keep my sabbaths, and reverence my sanctuary; I am the Lord.* Leviticus 19:30

FAMILY DISCUSSION

1. If we bring pictures and books to look at while we are in church, do you think we are learning to be quiet and to listen to God's Word? Or, are we learning NOT to pay attention to what our pastor tells us?

2. Are we able to know what the minister says if we whisper?

3. If you will read these passages from the Bible, you will find that the Word of God makes it plain that it is important and necessary to be *quiet* and attentive if we are to learn from the sermon what is preached to us: Numbers 9:8; I Samuel 9:27; 12:7; Job 37:14; Psalm 46:10; Zephaniah 1:7; Zechariah 2:13.

27

GROW-UP PLANS

"I'm going to be the first lady president of the United States when I grow up," declared Ann one day.

"I'm going to be a pilot and fly a jet plane," said Mark.

"Well, *I'm* going to run a big shovel and dig basements for houses when I grow up," decided Paul. "Or, maybe I'll drive one of those great big caterpillar tractors and help build roads."

Mom and Dad smiled. "What about you two," asked Dad of Stephen and Melissa. "What are you going to do when you grow up?"

Melissa shrugged her shoulders. "Oh, I suppose I'll get married. But I won't unless I can have a *pink* house."

Dad winked at her. "You mean to tell me, young lady, that if some big nice beautiful man who had a big nice beautiful white house wanted to marry you that you wouldn't marry him unless he got his house painted pink?"

"That's exactly right," insisted Melissa. "The house has to be pink."

"Well, Mother," said Dad, "some day you and I will

go to see grandchildren who live in a pink house. Now we are certain of that much. How about you, Steve? What will you live in? A purple house?"

Stephen's face was serious. "I don't know what kind of house I want to live in. Guess I've never thought much about that. And I keep changing my mind about what I want to do with my life."

"You wouldn't want to be a history teacher, would you?" Mom asked mischievously.

"No, thanks!" Just the day before Stephen had completed his eighth grade examinations. His teacher had told him he passed all tests, easily, even the history one. But Stephen still had no liking for the study of history.

Now he rubbed his forehead thoughtfully. "Sometimes I want to be a farmer, and just stay at Happy Acres all my life. Then again, I want to be a doctor, or a medical missionary. Then sometimes I'd like to be a governor or a judge. Something that really amounts to something. I'd like to do something—well, something great and important."

Dad turned to his eldest son with earnest face. "You know, Steve, I'm pleased to hear that you want to do something that is great and important. If you read stories about truly great people, though, you'll find out they never set out to make themselves great. They became great—well, you might say, almost by accident. People that decide they're going to be great—they never do, though they may succeed in attracting a lot of attention.

"You name some of the men you admire, Steve, the ones you think are really great—and we'll see what made them great."

"Well, I guess one of the greatest Americans was Abra-

94

ham Lincoln. *He* didn't plan to be great," said Stephen.
"And there's George Washington Carver."

"Yes," agreed Dad. "Carver was born a Negro slave.
He set out to help his people. He got so busy finding ways
to help them that he became one of the world's greatest
scientists. He was a very humble, God-fearing man.

"Now, Stevie, what man can you think of that is living
today, that you admire, and that many thousands of people over the world admire? Yet this man doesn't hold any
great office. He has no great title, but serves in a jungle."

"Oh, I know," replied Stephen, "that would be Albert
Schweitzer."

"Yes, Schweitzer. When he was a young man, he was
already an accomplished organist. He could have gone on
giving wonderful concerts all his life, and he would have
made a big name for himself as one of the world's finest
musicians. But we think of Schweitzer today as one of
the greatest men in the world because he turned his back
on fame, and instead he spent years to train himself to
become a medical missionary so that he could go to Lambarene in Africa and become a servant to those jungle
people who could certainly give him no reward. He even
had to earn money to build his own hospital—and he did
that by giving organ concerts in Europe. Now the whole
world has high respect for this humble man because it is
as Jesus once said, that the *greatest* men are the ones
who become *servants* among us.

"People don't become great because they want to be
great. Schweitzer never intended to make himself great
by going to Lambarene. All he thought about was that
those poor people in the jungles had no doctor. He just
forgot about himself. You might say that he laid down

95

his life in service to those jungle people—and then, as the Bible promises, Schweitzer found a greater life was his.

"I notice, Stevie, that you've been reading about some of the world's most wonderful people—Helen Keller, Florence Nightingale, David Livingstone, and others. You'll find their lives show what Jesus meant when He said, 'He that is greatest among you shall be your servant'" (Matt. 23:11).

"I suppose," observed Ann, "even if I did get to be the first woman president of the United States—just being the president wouldn't make me great."

"No," said Dad, "you would have an important *office*. But whether *you* would be a great woman president would depend on whether *you* had become a great servant in your heart. 'As a man thinketh in his heart, so is he'" (Prov. 23:7).

MEMORY VERSE: *But he that is greatest among you shall be your servant.* Matthew 23:11

FAMILY DISCUSSION

1. Think of people that you most admire and respect. Are they folks that "get from others before others get from them" or are they more likely to follow the Golden Rule?

2. Who do you think are some of the greatest people that have ever lived? Tell why you think each such person is great. Do you find that your choices of great people have been servants of their fellowmen?

28

GRAMPS HAGLUND AGAIN

"Mr. Haglund came back to the Rest Home Friday," Mom announced as the family settled around the Sunday dinner table, "and Dad is going to bring him out here for supper today."

There was no cheering from the Johnson youngsters when they heard this news. For a moment, there was silence, then Mark groaned in dismay and Melissa pleaded, "Oh, let's not try any more to adopt *him* for a grandfather!"

Dad looked at the glum faces about him and said, "Mother and I have decided that since Mr. Haglund doesn't seem to enjoy having children around, we won't ask you to help us entertain him today. So, if you don't want to be with us and Mr. Haglund this afternoon, that's all right."

There were several big sighs of relief around the table. Then Ann said, softly, "I'd just as soon stay with you and Mr. Haglund."

Stephen stared at his sister in amazement, then exclaimed, "If you still think you can make a nice grandpa out of that guy, you must be some sort of lady Job!"

That afternoon, when Mr. Haglund arrived, all the children except Ann were playing in the barn loft. Ann could see that their supper guest was about as grumpy as ever. When she set a large tin can beside his chair, he did not say "Thank you," but only rumbled in his throat and squinted one eye in her direction.

Dad tried to talk about the weather, about the news he had heard on the radio, about crops—but nothing seemed to interest Mr. Haglund.

Then Mom asked him, "Do you have any relatives, Mr. Haglund? Any family?"

"I came from Norway when I was seventeen," said Mr. Haglund, very slowly. "All my people are there. But I had a wife. Three little ones. They were killed. All of them. In a railroad accident. Forty-seven years ago."

Ann saw the old man look out the window and far away beyond the wheat field of rustling green. She could see that it hurt—still—for him to talk about his wife and the three little ones that had been killed. She saw a tear sparkle in one squinting eye. His voice was raspy when he said, "My wife—she was a good woman. She went to church. My kids—they were so little. And they were killed."

Ann wanted to cry. She looked at Mom and knew her mother's tender heart ached, too, for this lonely old man with the bristly hair and grumpy ways. She heard Mom saying, gently, "Oh, I am so sorry, Mr. Haglund. Forty-seven years is a long time to be alone."

"Yes," said the old man, his lips tightening, "a long time."

GRAMPS HAGLUND

That evening as the Johnsons and their guest seated themselves about the supper table, Ann sat beside Mr. Haglund. After praying for him for many days, her dislike for him had vanished. And now that she had heard his sad story, she wanted so much to help him in his loneliness.

Throughout the rather quiet meal, Mr. Haglund paid no attention to Ann, but somehow she felt certain that he did not *mind* having her next to him.

When he was ready to leave, he stood in the doorway and he looked first at Mom, and then straight at Ann, and said something that made her heart beat joyfully, "It is good to come here. I do not feel so alone—here!"

MEMORY VERSE: *Bear ye one another's burdens, and so fulfil the law of Christ.* Galatians 6:2

FAMILY DISCUSSION

1. Do *you* think that Mr. Haglund will learn to become a nice grandfather for the Johnsons?
2. What have Ann and Mom done to make him feel more friendly toward them?
3. When we know someone who is lonely, or someone who has trouble, what should we do? (Romans 15:1; Galatians 6:2; Hebrews 13:3)

29

A NEW CAR FOR THE HACKLEYS

The sun beat warmly down on Ann, Mark, and Stephen as they pulled weeds from the long rows of potatoes. Most of the time the three were on their knees. They were hot and tired and their knees sore, when they heard the purr of a car coming down the road alongside the potato field.

They raised their heads to see a sleek and shining red sedan—and in it sat Lucia Hackley and her parents.

"Hello, there," called Mrs. Hackley. Mr. Hackley nodded his handsome head, and Lucia waved a white-gloved hand elegantly at Ann as the car swept by.

"Why, they've got a brand-new car," exclaimed Stephen and Mark in one breath.

Ann stood up. With a grimy hand she pulled a wisp of stray hair from her eyes and said, "Hmm, I can just *hear* Lucia telling how simply *lovely* their car is, and how simply *awful*-looking *ours* is!"

"Why, come to think about it," said Stephen, "they get a new car about every year."

"And *our* car is five years old," observed Mark.

A NEW CAR

"How is it that the Hackleys can afford a new car, and we can't? We have a bigger farm," reasoned Stephen. "We have more crops. We milk many more cows than they do. I *know* Dad makes more money than the Hackleys do on their farm."

"Yes," agreed Ann, "and they don't have chickens or eggs to sell. Lucia is always telling me *she* doesn't have to clean eggs like *I* do."

"Well, for one thing," decided Mark, "they don't have as big a family. They just have Lucia. Dad has six of us to support."

Suddenly, there was Mom coming with a big thermos. "Hi," she called. "How about some limeade with ice cubes?"

In a few minutes, the four had settled in the shade of a tree. As they thirstily drank, the three weed-pullers told Mom about the Hackleys' new car.

"Mom," asked Stephen, "how come we can't afford a new car if the Hackleys can? We certainly make more money than they do."

"Yes," his mother replied, "we do make more money than they do. But we may have to wait another year before we can buy that station wagon we all want."

"But why?" urged Ann.

"Well now," asked Mom, "why should we get a new car? Because the Hackleys have gotten a new car?"

The three weed-pullers looked at one another, but none wanted to answer.

"We know," continued Mom, "that the Lord will supply all our *needs*—and when we really need another car, I am certain we'll be able to get one. But the Lord hasn't promised to supply us with luxuries, or with things we

want just because our neighbors have such things. You know, there are a lot of people who are unhappy because they are working and worrying so much in order to be just as stylish or as up-and-coming as their neighbors."

Then she asked, "What would be a *good* reason for our getting a new car?"

"Well," said Mark, "us kids keep getting bigger and bigger. And our car stays the same size. It's getting so

102

that we're packed like sardines when we all get inside the car."

"And it *is* wearing out," added Stephen.

"There," chuckled Mom, "you have two good reasons for our wanting to get a station wagon."

"But, Mom," insisted Stephen, "I still can't see why Dad couldn't *afford* a new car as long as the Hackleys who earn less money can afford a new car every year or so."

"Stephen, what do we do with the money we earn from our farm?"

"Well, there's food and clothing for us all. Fuel in the winter. It costs a lot for machinery, and to run the farm. There's insurance, and I know Dad keeps putting away money for us kids for an education. We tithe to the church. Why, just what we give to the church every year—if we used that, we wouldn't be riding around stuffed into our old car. The Hackleys don't tithe—they just don't go to church, hardly ever."

"We mustn't consider our giving to the church according to what certain of our neighbors may or may not do in that respect, Steve. Would we be doing the Lord's will for us if we spent our tithe for new cars?"

Stephen shook his head.

"No, we couldn't be Christians and not give to the Lord's work. Having a new car every year couldn't possibly bring us the joy that is ours in the Lord when we help Him with His Kingdom building. Remember what we sing in church when we take up the offering? Let's sing it now, and perhaps we'll understand better about this business of giving to the Lord."

There in the potato field, Mom and the three weed-pulling Johnsons sang:

> *"We give Thee but Thine own*
> *Whate'er the gift may be;*
> *All that we have is Thine alone,*
> *A trust, O Lord, from Thee."*

Mom stayed and helped pull the rest of the weeds. As they walked home together, none of the Johnsons mentioned the Hackley's new car. It wasn't important any more after Mom had reminded them that all the world, and all "they that dwell therein" (Ps. 24:1), belonged to the Lord. A new station wagon would be nice to have, and it would come when they needed it.

For now, it was best to remember: "But seek ye first the kingdom of God, and his righteousness, and all these things shall be added unto you" (Matt. 6:33).

MEMORY VERSE: *But seek ye first the kingdom of God, and his righteousness; and all these things shall be added unto you.* Matthew 6:33

FAMILY DISCUSSION

1. What is the most important gift that we can give to the Lord? (Ourselves—see II Corinthians 8:5)

2. In the Old Testament, we find that the Hebrew people were advised to give a tithe of their earnings—that is, one-tenth of their herds or crops—to the Lord. What does God's word tell us in the New Testament about how much we should give to the Lord? (I Corinthians 16:2; II Corinthians 9:7)

30

THE HOUSE WITH EYES

It was time for another of Dad's stories, and this one, he promised, was about some folks who lived in the House With Eyes.

"Out west on the banks of the Missouri river, in a place that is now flooded by the Garrison Dam reservoir there was once an Indian village called Like-a-Fish-Hook. Close by was an army post, Fort Berthold.

"Many years ago, before railroads were built out this way, paddle-wheeled steamers used to sail up and down the Missouri river carrying soldiers and army supplies to the forts along the river. These steamers also carried gold prospectors and hunters and explorers. Back in the summer of 1876, a young missionary and his bride came up on a river steamer and they got off at Fort Berthold.

"More than a thousand Indians lived at Like-a-Fish-Hook village nearby. And a lot of them stood watching as this young Charles Hall got off the steamer. They watched this missionary with unfriendly faces—because most of the white people these Indians had known had treated them unjustly. The Indians looked so unfriendly

105

that the captain of the boat said to Missionary Hall, 'You'd better take my gun, or those Indians will kill you.'

"But Mr. Hall answered, 'My weapon is the Word of God.'

"Hall built his own little house close to Like-a-Fish-Hook village. And because it had windows, the Indians called it the House With Eyes. These Indians would come right up to the windows and look right inside at the Hall family.

"It was hard for Mr. Hall to learn the Indians' language, and the Indians were slow to make friends with him. But when a baby was born to the Halls, Mrs. Hall put the baby into the baby carriage, and the Halls promenaded with it among the big round earth lodges in the Indian village. The Indian mothers and children crowded around to see the little white baby and they all smiled. From that time on, the Indians were more friendly.

"But no matter how often Missionary Hall would invite them, none of the Indian children would come inside the House With Eyes for a visit.

"Then an old Indian chief called White Shield told Hall, 'If you will feed the children, they will come to your house like flies after syrup.' So the Halls prepared a good meal, and invited the children. From then on, the children would come to the House With Eyes, especially when there was something to eat, and Missionary Hall would then teach them about Jesus.

"For sixty years, Reverend Hall lived with the Indians and became their trusted friend. They built their own churches where he could come and preach to them.

"And you know, that summer that Missionary Hall

106

came to Like-a-Fish-Hook village, General Custer went out to meet the Sioux Indians in Montana with swords and guns and he and all his men were killed by the Indians. Mr. Hall came out to meet the Indians in Christian love—his only weapon was the Word of God, and he lived peacefully and happily with the Indians to the end of his life.

"Missionary Hall knew that three things will always last—that's faith, hope, and love, and he knew that 'the greatest of these is love'" (I Cor. 13:13).

"Yes," Mom added, "and Hall brought with him 'the helmet of salvation, and the sword of the Spirit, which is the Word of God'" (Eph. 6:17).

MEMORY VERSE: *So faith, hope, love abide, these three; but the greatest of these is love.* I Corinthians 13:13 (RSV)

FAMILY DISCUSSION

1. Why were the Indians first suspicious and unfriendly toward Missionary Hall?

2. If you had been an Indian at Like-a-Fish-Hook village, would you have felt the same way toward the missionary as others there felt?

3. It is not fair to judge all people of a certain race by the way some of their race may behave. When we meet people of another race, how may we avoid making the same mistakes in judging them as these Indians made when they first met and judged Missionary Hall? (I Peter 2:12)

4. In our church, do we have missionaries working among the Indians? Can you name any such missionaries and tell where they work?

5. What boy of long, long ago met a powerful enemy without fear even though he had no sword? (I Samuel 45:47.) Did this boy have the same kind of faith as Missionary Hall had?

31

SUGAR AND CREAM FOR PAUL

Quickly, Paul poured the cereal bowl half full of sugar. Then, from a pitcher he almost brimmed the bowl with rich, thick cream. With a spoon, he stirred this until the sugar and cream were well mixed.

He put the cream pitcher back into the refrigerator, the sugar bowl in the cupboard. Then, smacking his lips, he carried the bowl of sugar and cream down to the cool basement and greedily ate.

His stomach was round and hard when he carried the emptied bowl back to the kitchen. There he rinsed it and his spoon in the sink. He dried them and put them away, so there would be no tell-tale signs of the feast he had just sneaked.

Once in a while, Mom would fix Paul's favorite supper—slices of bread spread with cream and sprinkled with sugar. Sometimes, when he asked, she would give him a small saucer of sugar and cream. But never until now had he ever had as much sugar and cream as he *liked* to have.

He slipped out of the house. He didn't care to go to

SUGAR AND CREAM

the garden where Mom and the rest of the family were busy. So he hurried out and found his red hen instead, and fed her and her chicks some cracked corn.

Suddenly, he heard his name called, and he almost jumped into the air. It was Ann saying, "Paul, come and get some ice cream. We're having some ice cream!"

Ice cream! Paul liked ice cream even better than sugar and cream. On a hot summer afternoon, nothing ever tasted as good as ice cream.

But this time, he didn't feel like running as fast as he usually did when ice cream was announced.

In the kitchen he found his sisters and brothers already feasting on home-made ice cream. As Paul sat down, Mom set a big dish of delicious ice cream before him and beamed at him, "There you are, Son. Have a good time!"

Paul said, "Thank you," but he didn't look at Mom. He picked up his spoon and ate slowly. He began to wonder if he'd ever be able to eat all of that big mound of ice cream. The other children were having second helpings—and Mark his third helping—when at last Paul downed his last spoonful.

Right away, Mom was there to give him a second helping.

"Oh, no, please," begged Paul. "I don't care for any more, Mom. Thanks."

Mom looked at him in astonishment. "No more ice cream? Well, I'm surprised!" And the sisters and brothers all stared at him, hardly able to believe that Paul would refuse a second helping of ice cream.

Soon he went quietly to the bathroom, then on up to his own room. He felt miserable, and had lain on his bed only a few minutes when Mom appeared, looking anxious. She asked him, "Don't you feel well?"

"Oh, I'm all right."

"You don't have any pain anywhere?"

"No."

"Maybe you'd like to take a nap."

A nap wasn't something that Paul ordinarily cared about, but right now there wasn't anything he'd rather do. "Uh huh, I'd like to take a nap."

Mom's eyes blinked with wonder, but she only said, "Then you just take a nap."

Soon after, Paul was asleep. He awoke when the dinner gong rang for supper. He got up, hurried to the bathroom, and then downstairs to the kitchen where the family was sitting down to a supper of home-made bread spread with cream and sprinkled with sugar.

Mom smiled at him, "Hi, Paulie. You had a nice long nap. Now you can have your favorite supper—bread with cream and sugar."

But after Grace had been said, and Dad began to

110

cover a slice of bread with thick cream for him, Paul wanted to get up from the table and run away. He couldn't bear even a spoonful of that cream!

He hung his head and begged, "Please, Dad, I don't want any supper."

Mom was alarmed when she overheard this. "Paulie, you can't be well!"

"Oh, I'm all right. I'm—just—not hungry."

"Would you like to go back to bed?"

"I guess I'd just as soon."

In his room, away from the sight of cream and sugar, Paul felt better. However, he kept thinking about that bowl full of sugar and cream that he had eaten, and he knew that no one—not even Mom—had guessed. Nobody in the family would ever be able to find out.

A little while later, Mom and Dad came up to see him. Mom felt of his forehead and remarked, "Well, you don't have any fever."

Dad sat on the bed beside Paul. "Something the matter, Son? It just is not like you not to want to have any supper—especially when it's bread with sugar and cream."

Paul felt sick at the thought of the sugar and cream, and he wondered if he'd ever want to eat a supper of bread with cream and sugar again. Certainly he wouldn't want another bowl plumb full of sugar and cream, ever!

Suddenly, he wanted to get rid of this guilty feeling that had filled him ever since he had sneaked that sugar and cream. That guilty feeling was much worse than to have the sick, stuffy feeling in his stomach.

He burst into tears, and crawled into his father's lap, sobbing, "I sneaked—a whole bowl of sugar and cream —and ate it all—this afternoon."

111

"Oh," said Mom, with lifted eyebrows, "just before we had that ice cream?"

"Yes, just before we had that ice cream. And I'm sorry."

"Poor Paulie-boy!" Dad held him tight. Then soon Dad was shaking with laughter. First thing Paul knew, *he* was laughing, too. And he wasn't feeling sick any more. He had told on himself—and he could laugh again. It was ever so much better than keeping that guilty feeling!

MEMORY VERSE: *If we confess our sins, he is faithful and just to forgive us our sins, and to cleanse us from all unrighteousness.* I John 1:9

FAMILY DISCUSSION

1. Why didn't Paul want to go out where his mother was, after he had eaten the sugar and cream?

2. Can a guilty feeling make you sick?

3. Criminals have always tried to commit the "perfect crime"—that is, do some wrong without anyone else ever finding it out. Had Paul managed to steal without anyone in the family learning about it, before he told on himself?

4. Once in a while, a bad person is able to steal or to kill without ever being caught. But what is it that the criminal can never run or hide from? (His conscience—Psalm 32:3; 38:4; John 8:9; Romans 2:15; I John 3:20)

5. Who, besides Paul, knew of his stealing, even before Paul confessed it to his parents? (Jeremiah 23:24; Proverbs 15:3; Psalm 139:1-3; Luke 12:2)

6. As soon as Paul had told his parents about his wrongdoing, his guilty feeling was gone and he was happy. Is this the way with us when we confess our sins to God? (I John 1:9; Proverbs 28:13)

32

SURPRISING NEWS

Returning from a visit to the Reynolds farm, the four oldest Johnson children trooped down the road to Happy Acres Farm. As they neared the vacant Blanchard farmstead, Mark cried out in surprise, "Hey, looks like there's some people moving in there!"

Excited over the prospect of having new neighbors just half a mile down the road, the four stared eagerly as they walked by the farmstead which was almost hidden by a grove of trees. They saw a small blue car parked in the weed-grown driveway, and a large van backed to the door of the little brown house.

For five years, since old Mr. Blanchard had died, no one had lived in the little brown house. One of the neighbors had rented the fields and the pasture land of the small farm—and boards had covered the windows of the buildings.

Eager to tell what they had seen, the Johnson children raced home. Stephen was the first to burst into the kitchen and report, "Mom, we're going to have neighbors —down at the Blanchard place!"

"Are you sure?"

"Yes, there's a moving van—and we could see them unloading furniture into the house."

Mark and Ann now reached the kitchen—and Melissa came puffing behind them.

"Boy, I wonder if there'll be any kids in the family. Sure hope there's a boy my age," said Mark.

"And a girl my age," added Ann.

Mom had a puzzled look on her face. "Well, if we're going to have neighbors, we should do something to welcome them. For one thing, I know it will be hard for them to do any cooking the first few days. So we could send them a hot dish or something while they are getting settled."

"I'll take the hot dish over," offered Mark.

"Me, too," said Ann.

"But we don't know how many there are in the family, or if they'll even be staying there tonight—" began Mom.

"I can run over and find out," suggested Mark.

"I want to go over with Mark," said Melissa. So did Stephen and Ann and Paul and Beth.

Mom shook her head. "No, it wouldn't be considerate to have six children barging in on folks trying to get moved into that little house. It will be enough to have just one go. Mark was the first to offer, so we'll let him go."

Mark snatched up the sandwich Mom had fixed, and was off in a flash.

Ann pouted. "Oh, it seems like it's always Mark that gets to go."

"Remember who stayed home when a certain girl was in town shopping?" Mom reminded her.

SURPRISING NEWS

Ann nodded. That was the day Mark had broken the lamp chimney.

But she sulked over her sandwich and a cookie. When she saw Stephen reach to the cookie plate and take the last cookie, she scolded, "Mom, Steve's had two cookies —and the rest of us just got one apiece."

"Ann," said Mom, "we can't ever expect to get everything evened up. There'll always be somebody who gets more cookies than we do. And always somebody who doesn't get as many cookies as we do. And as long as we keep counting cookies, and watching that we get whatever somebody else gets we are not going to be very happy. That's just not the Christian way to live with others. We'll be much happier if we are 'kindly affectioned one to another with brotherly love, in honor preferring one another' [Rom. 12:10]. To prefer one another means to put the other person first, to love the other person so that you are glad to let him have a cookie— or something that you may not have had yourself.

"Just think of the fun we had playing secret sister and secret brother—because then we were kindly affectioned one to another. I'm sure you won't be envious of Mark —or of Steve because of that cookie—if you'll stop right now to think of something good that you can do for one of your brothers."

Ann got up and went outside. She ran down to the chick shelters to do one of Mark's chores for him—and filled all the mash hoppers, and was surprised to find her envy all gone.

Meanwhile, Mark reached the Blanchard place. There was not a sound to be heard as he walked into the yard. The van was gone. So was the blue car. The boards were off the windows of the house, but no one answered his knock at the door.

MEMORY VERSE: *Love one another with brotherly affection; outdo one another in showing honor.* Romans 12:10 (RSV)

FAMILY DISCUSSION

1. If we were to get new neighbors, what are some things that we could do for them?

2. What are some ways in which we can "outdo one another in showing honor" right here in our home? In church? In school?

33

WAGGLING TONGUES

Each day, one of the Johnson children would run down the road to the Blanchard place to see if the new neighbors had come. But each time there was no blue car parked in the drive, no one who answered the rap at the door.

No one in the Pleasant Valley neighborhood knew anything about the new neighbors except that Mr. Gordon who had rented the Blanchard farm had learned that the new owner was a man by the name of Charles Turner and that he lived in Minneapolis or St. Paul.

Then one Saturday, Ann and Melissa returned from an afternoon with the Schramm twins—and they had plenty to report about the new neighbors. Melissa was the first to reach the kitchen door, and her eyes fairly popped as she cried, "Mom, what do you suppose? The people who bought the Blanchard place—why, the man is a—a—a—"

"A *jailbird*," supplied Ann. "Mrs. Schramm's cousin from the Cities was there visiting, and she says she knows about the Charles Turners. She said that Mr. Turner has been in jail several times, and she was pretty sure he'd been in the penitentiary, too!"

"Now, now, Ann," objected Mom, "are you sure you have heard this right?"

"Yes, it is too, so," agreed Melissa. "I heard that lady from the Cities say so. She was sure it was the same Charles Turner. And she said we'd just better stay clear of those Turners!"

"Yes," added Ann, "and Mrs. Schramm says *they* aren't going to have anything to do with such people. Those Turners have four boys—and Mrs. Schramm's cousin says they're all bad boys and they'll just be jailbirds like their dad. And Mrs. Schramm said, too, that nobody ever saw Mr. Turner come out here to look at the Blanchard place before he bought it, so she's been suspicious he's just—"

Mom put her arms around the two excited girls. "I think we've repeated enough now about people we really don't know a thing about. There might well be several Charles Turners living in the Cities. The Charles Turner that is coming to live on the Blanchard place may well be someone Mrs. Schramm's cousin knows exactly nothing about. Let's not forget that the Bible says, 'Thou shalt not raise a false report' [Exod. 23:1]. How would you girls like it if folks told bad things about you that weren't so? Even if it should be true that Mr. Turner has been in jail, or even in the penitentiary, maybe he's coming out here to live a better life. It wouldn't be Christian of us to put a stumblingblock in his way [Rom. 14:13] by making it hard for him to live a decent life."

"Well, what should we do about it?" asked Ann.

WAGGLING TONGUES

"We are not going to repeat to *anyone* what you have heard this afternoon," said Mom, very firmly.

"But are we going to keep running over to the Blanchard place to see if they've come? I'm scared to now!"

"Don't worry about that. Dad and I will take care of it."

That same evening, the Johnsons piled into the old sedan to go for a visit at the Reynolds farm. As they drove past the Blanchard place, Ann squealed with excitement for she spied a blue car parked beside the little brown house. And that little blue car, she decided, looked exactly like the kind of car that a jailbird would drive!

MEMORY VERSE: *He who loves his brother abides in the light, and in it there is no cause for stumbling.* I John 2:10 (RSV)

FAMILY DISCUSSION

1. Read Romans 14:13. What are ways in which you may be a stumblingblock to your friends or neighbors?
2. If the Charles Turner that comes to live on the Blanchard place is *not* the jailbird that Mrs. Schramm's cousin knows, what do you think Ann and Melissa should do?
3. If you should have playmates or neighbors that do evil, what can you do to help them?
4. Which of the Ten Commandments are we breaking when we gossip about other people?

34

HELLO TO THE TURNERS

The blue car in the Blanchard yard was the cause of many excited remarks as the Johnsons continued down the road. Suddenly, Mom suggested, "Dad, let's drive back and stop long enough to say Hello to the Turners."

Melissa and Ann shrank against the car cushions, frightened at the thought of actually meeting the "jailbird." But the other children who had heard none of the gossip about the new neighbors were eager to meet the new family.

Dad turned at the crossroads. Soon the Johnson car was parked near the little brown house.

Ann squeezed her hands nervously as she watched her father and mother get out of the car and step up on the front porch. Dad knocked at the door.

It seemed to Ann that it was a long time before the door opened. Jailbird people would be suspicious, and wouldn't be quick to open a door!

She heard a man's voice saying, "Hello."

Then she heard Mom say, "We're the Peter Johnsons, your neighbors up the road half a mile. We just wanted to stop a few minutes to say Hello and to welcome you to our neighborhood."

From inside the house came a woman's voice, but Ann could not tell what she was saying.

Soon the door closed behind Mom and Dad.

While her brothers looked curiously about, hoping to see signs of future friends, Ann fearfully hoped that her parents would soon come safely out of that house. She was frightened at the idea of Mom and Dad being in there with the jailbird and his wife—and very likely, with those four bad sons.

"Say, look over there—on the porch," exclaimed Mark. "Look at those guns! Three of them!"

Ann looked in the same direction. She stared in terror. Three big guns! She scarcely heard Stephen saying, "The Turners must like to hunt. That's a rifle and a couple of double-barreled shotguns."

Ann had her own ideas about the guns. Of course, a jailbird family would have guns. But not for hunting ducks and pheasants!

She put her hands to her face and began to cry with fright.

"Why, Ann," exclaimed Stephen in surprise, "what in the world is the matter with you?"

Ann had no answer. But Melissa piped out, "I know! She's *scared!* She's scared—of the—jailbird."

"*Jailbird,*" puzzled Mark and Stephen together. "What do you mean?"

"Oh, we promised not—to tell—anybody."

"Not to tell *what?*"

"Oh—we can't tell anybody—*what!*" By now both Ann and Melissa were crying.

121

At just that moment, Mom and Dad stepped out on the porch, followed by Mr. and Mrs. Turner. Ann could see only four blurry figures because her eyes were so full of tears, but she did hear Mom saying very plainly, "Goodbye now. I'll be sending a hot dish over for you folks tomorrow. And then we'll all see you Sunday morning."

MEMORY VERSE: *He who digs a pit will fall into it, and a stone will come back upon him who starts it rolling.* Proverbs 26:27 (RSV)

FAMILY DISCUSSION

1. Would the sight of the guns frighten Ann as much if she had never heard the jailbird story about Mr. Turner?
2. Do you think Mr. Turner is a jailbird? Why or why not?
3. Read Proverbs 26:22 (King James). Do you think this proverb applies to Ann and Melissa?
4. Can you think of times when you have suffered because of talebearing?
5. What is the best thing to do when we hear someone saying evil about another person?
6. Even though an evil report may be true, what should we do or not do about it?

35

THE TRUTH ABOUT THE TURNERS

"The Turners are going to make wonderful neighbors!" announced Mom as the Johnsons drove on their way to the Reynolds farm. "Mr. Turner has been a school principal all his life, and he's come here to retire because both of them have always wanted to live on a little farm. Both of them were born on farms in North Dakota. Mrs. Turner has been a piano teacher. They are Christian people, and they are coming with us to church on Sunday."

Ann and Melissa looked first at their mother, and then at each other. "Guess I sure wasted a lot of being scared," whispered Melissa to her sister.

"Don't they have any kids to play with?" Paul inquired of his mother.

"Well, hardly," replied Mom. "They have one son. He's married and lives in Chicago. They expect him here for a visit this fall—during hunting season because he just loves to hunt pheasant.

"But even though the Turners don't have children your age, you'll have happy times with them. I think they are a delightful couple, and I'm just thrilled to have them as neighbors. You children will be interested to know that they are going to raise a few Angora rabbits, and they are going to have some goats because Mr. Turner prefers to drink goat milk. They are going to raise some pedigreed dogs, too."

All the way to the Reynolds farm, Mom and Dad reported happily about what they had learned about their new neighbors.

Somehow, Ann did not have as much fun as usual with the Reynolds children. She kept remembering the jailbird story, and she was glad when at last they were home, and Mom came tiptoe into her room to say goodnight.

"Oh, Mom," Ann whispered, "I wish I hadn't told that jailbird story!"

"Yes, I'm sure you do. But let's see what you can think to do to help make it right."

"I could go over and apologize to the Turners."

"Do you think that would make matters right?"

Ann pondered a while, then said, "Maybe it would do more good if I went and told the Schramm twins the truth about the Turners—so they won't go spreading that jailbird story further."

So it was that when Mr. Johnson drove to town on an errand the next day, Ann rode with him as far as the Schramm farm. It didn't take Ann long to tell the twins and their mother that Mr. Turner was *not* a jailbird, but that instead the new neighbors were good and wonderful people. When she had finished, she said, "I hope you girls didn't go tell anybody else that jailbird story."

"Oh," said one of the twins, "we told Gertie Gordon and Patsy Smith."

The Gordons lived across the road from the Schramms. So Ann and the twins went there to tell the Gordons that Mr. Turner was not a jailbird but a respectable retired schoolteacher.

They discovered that Gertie Gordon had already told Sharon Oberholtz.

So Ann and the twins walked half a mile down the road to the Oberholtz farm. There they found that Sharon had told the jailbird story to Grace Lawler. And she had told it on the party line, and there was no telling how many people might have "listened in." To make matters even worse, Sharon had thought that *she* had heard that both *Mr.* and *Mrs.* Turner were jailbirds, and that was what she had told Grace.

Wearily, Ann and the twins trudged back to the Schramm farm so that Ann would be there by the time her father returned from town.

As she rode home with her father, Ann told him how the jailbird story had spread, and how it had gotten worse with each telling.

Dad said, quietly, "Well, the next time you hear someone telling something like this jailbird story about someone you don't know, I'm sure you'll remember this little verse. 'Even so, the tongue is a little member and boasteth great things. Behold how great a matter a little fire kindleth'" (James 3:5).

MEMORY VERSE: *So the tongue is a little member and boasteth great things. How great a forest is set ablaze by a small fire.* James 3:5 (RSV)

FAMILY DISCUSSION

1. Next time you have a party at your house, try the gossip game. Write down a sentence. Then whisper that same sentence to the first person. He whispers *exactly what he heard* to the next in line. This continues until each person has listened once and then whispered. Then have the last person say out loud what *he* has heard. Read the sentence you had written down.

2. What does Mr. Johnson mean to tell Ann when he says, "Behold how great a matter a little fire kindleth"?

3. Here are Proverbs that teach us about our tongues: Proverbs 12:18-19; 15:4; 21:23.

36

MARK GETS THE GRUMPS

"Mark must have gotten up on the wrong side of his bed today," said Stephen to his father, one morning. "Boy, has he ever got the grumps! Nothing suits him."

It was plain for anyone to see when Mark came in and took his place at the table that he was feeling cross. So Steve was not at all surprised when Dad announced, after Grace, "We're going to play the Thank You game today while we eat. We'll start with the youngest this time."

The Thank You game was one of Dad's inventions. As each person's turn came, he would tell of something for which he was thankful—something which no one else had yet mentioned. The object of the game was to see who could keep counting his blessings the longest.

Now little Beth started the game with, "Glad I have a kitty."

Paul was next with, "Glad I have my red hen."

Melissa said, "I'm thankful for Mom and Dad."

Ann was thankful for the new dress Mom was making for her.

Mark hardly looked up from his plate as he said, "Well, I'm glad for this good food."

Dad chuckled at this. Mark, looking up at his father, almost smiled. But he couldn't help grinning when Stephen announced, "Well, I'm glad I've got my sweet brother Mark."

Mom was glad for having the whole family together. Dad was glad for home.

Around and around the table, the blessings were counted. By the time the meal was eaten, no one had dropped out of the game—not even Beth. And so, as usual, there was no winner.

But when Mark stood up from the table, he was no longer grumpy for he had counted too many blessings to stay grumpy.

MEMORY VERSE: *In everything give thanks: for this is the will of God in Christ Jesus.* I Thessalonians 5:18

FAMILY DISCUSSION

1. What was one of Christ's regular habits? (Matthew 14:19; 15:36; Mark 8:1-10)

2. Let each one of us start each day by giving thanks to God. When we get up in the morning, too, let's see how many blessings we can count—then we'll be surprised how much happier each day will be for us.

37

DINNER GUESTS AT HAPPY ACRES

Ann thrilled with happiness as she sat next to Mrs. Turner in church. Just beyond Melissa was Mr. Turner, and snuggled close to him was Paul. Beth was on Dad's lap as usual, and Mark and Stephen on the other side of him. It was just like having grandparents with them in church, Ann decided.

After services, the little blue car followed the Johnson's old sedan to Happy Acres Farm. And when they had all gathered about the big dining table, it was Mr. Turner who was asked to pray. Through the meal, the talk was gay and full of laughter as Mr. Turner told them what fun they were all going to have with frolicking goats and prancing kids and long-eared, pink-eyed rabbits and silky-haired cocker spaniel puppies.

After dinner, the kitchen crew worked as quietly as mice so they could hear the interesting conversation in the living room. Then, with the dishes done, Stephen, Mark and Ann were free to join the company. Mrs. Turner's eyes twinkled as she sat down at the piano, and Mr. Turner stood up and sang a gay little thank-you song to the kitchen crew.

No one—not even Beth—took a nap that afternoon. There were just too many happy things to do and to hear. The ten of them sang together, and when Mr. Turner told Beth some silly, funny stories about Beatrice, the Beautiful Bunny, everybody — even Dad — listened eagerly.

"Where," asked Mom, "do you get those delightful bunny stories, Mr. Turner?"

"Oh," chuckled Mr. Turner as he winked at Beth beside him, "Beatrice, the Beautiful Bunny, tells them to me whenever her tummy is chuck full of delicious cabbage leaves."

It was Mr. Turner who was the champion croquet player of the afternoon. Mrs. Turner did not play croquet. Instead, she wandered off with Paul to visit with his red hen and her nine chicks. When the two of them came back, Paul's eyes were shining with some happy secret.

As the Turners drove away from Happy Acres, there were eight Johnsons hoping they would come back soon. And Ann exclaimed, "Oh, wouldn't *they* be wonderful grandparents to adopt? Only they—they don't *need* to be adopted. We couldn't do *anything* to help them be better. But, oh, how I wish we could have them for make-believe grandparents!"

"You know what?" asked Paul, "Mrs. Turner *is* my grandmother!"

"*Is* your grandmother? How come?"

"Well, she said—when we were looking at my red hen —that I should call her 'Grandmother' 'cause she doesn't

130

have any boy to call her 'Grandmother.' So you see, she *is* my grandmother already!"

"Maybe she'll have the rest of us, too," cried Melissa, clapping her hands.

Dad smiled. "Yes, Melissa, I rather think the Turners will have the rest of you for grandchildren, too."

"I've been praying every day for a grandmother or a grandfather some day," said Ann, "but I never thought such a wonderful grandmother and grandfather would just move in at the Blanchard place. Just like a miracle!"

Mom beamed. "Yes, remember the Lord's promise that 'before they call, I will answer; and while they are yet speaking, I will hear' [Isa. 65:24]. God has given us something even better than what you've been asking for, Ann. You thought it would be quite a while before you could find grandparents, and here they are already, when you thought you'd be praying a long time for them."

Even Stephen who had never thought much about this little-girl business of adopting grandparents was joyful at the thought of having a Grandmother and Grandfather Turner just down the road half a mile.

But even while Ann smiled happily about the Turner grandparents, she kept thinking quietly to herself that she wanted still another grandparent—a grandpa that hadn't been as easy to learn to love as the Turners.

MEMORY VERSE: *Therefore I tell you, whatever you ask in prayer, believe that you receive it, and you will.* Mark 11:24 (RSV)

FAMILY DISCUSSION

1. Can you think of times when, like Ann, you have been praying for something—and the answer to your prayer has

come sooner than you expected, and better than you had hoped for?

2. Can you think of times when you have prayed for something, and your prayer has never been answered? If you search the Scriptures, you will find there are several reasons why some of our prayers are not answered.

    a. Our prayer is selfish. (James 4:3)

    b. We do not pray in faith. (James 1:6-7)

    c. We may have an unconfessed sin (Psalm 66:18; Proverbs 1:28-29)

    d. We may be asking God for help while at the same time we fail to help those about us that *we* could help. (Proverbs 21:13)

    e. We do not respect God's law. (Proverbs 28:9)

    f. We are not saved through Christ. (Isaiah 59:2)

    g. It is not God's will that our prayer be answered. (II Corinthians 12:7-10)

3. How may we pray successfully?

    a. Contritely. (II Corinthians 7:14)

    b. Whole-heartedly. (Jeremiah 29:13)

    c. In faith. (Mark 11:24)

    d. As obedient children of God. (I John 3:22)

132

38

THE SHUFFLING MAN

In Woodbridge, one afternoon, the Johnsons parked their car in a side street just as Ann spotted a strange-appearing man come shuffling awkwardly down the side-walk. "Look," she said, "look at that queer fellow."

In a second, the Johnson children were staring at the man. Paul and Melissa began to snicker. The man's arm shook and wiggled about like the arms of a flapping scarecrow. He did not walk straight, but wobbled about. His face would twist as though he were trying to make funny faces. Paul and Melissa laughed aloud as the man came near.

But Dad's face was suddenly red. His eyes were very stern as he turned and said, "You—*hush!* That man is not to be laughed at!"

The giggling and snickering in the back seat stopped right away. One look at Dad was enough to show that they were doing something he thought was very wrong.

Mom had been busy with lacing Beth's shoes, so she had just caught sight of the shuffling man. Now she, too, turned to look at Paul and Melissa and whisper, "No, indeed, that man is not to be laughed at! We can be very thankful that none of our family is afflicted like he is!"

"What is it to be *afflicted*?" asked Melissa, sober now.

"You are afflicted if you are crippled, or if you are sick or hurt in some way. That man is afflicted because he can't get his hands or his feet or his face to do what he wants them to do. We call such a man a 'spastic' or he may have an affliction known as 'cerebral palsy.'"

"Yes," said Dad, "I remember a boy who lived in a town not far from where I grew up. He was a spastic. His throat muscles didn't work very well so it was hard for him to speak. Only a few people could understand what he said, and he would thrash his arms around because he just couldn't help it. He walked along something like the way this man does. Other children in that town would sometimes come behind him and mock him as he shuffled down the street. They thought they were being funny.

"Just because some people couldn't understand what this boy would say, they said he was stupid. They would even talk about him right in front of him as though he didn't have sense enough to understand the unkind things they were saying about him.

"He couldn't play games with the other boys, and so he was left to himself. He was very lonely, and his feelings were hurt many times by children who didn't know any better than to laugh at him because he was different from them. He suffered a great deal because grown folks, even church people, didn't show Christian compassion for him.

"Because he had almost no friends, and because he was an exceptionally bright boy, he read a great deal about history and geography and geology. He started a big stamp collection, and he became very much interested in rocks and stones. Even though it wasn't easy for him to get around on level ground, he would crawl around in the hills and ravines and study the rock and soil formations. And you know, this boy that some of the neighbors said was stupid won a scholarship in geology from a great university in the East.

"Now he has his doctor's degree, and he has a good job, and he has written a geology text that is used in colleges.

"Just remember that people like this poor man who just went down the street can't help the way they may look and act, and I'm sure you won't laugh the next time you see a person that is handicapped in some way. Let's always remember that no matter *how* a person may look or *how* a person may act, he has *feelings* just like we do."

"Yes," added Mom, "when we meet such poor or afflicted people, let's think of this verse from the Bible: 'Whoso stoppeth his ears at the cry of the poor, he also shall cry himself, but shall not be heard'" (Prov. 21:13).

MEMORY VERSE: *Blessed are the merciful, for they shall obtain mercy.* Matthew 5:7

FAMILY DISCUSSION

1. Do we have any handicapped people in our community? If there is, what can *we* do to help such a person live a happy life?

2. The best kind of help we can give a handicapped person is help that will help him to help himself. What do we mean by this?

3. What did Christ do for the handicapped people that he met? (Matthew 4:23-24; 8:1-4; 12:9-14; 15:29-31)

4. In many heathen lands, it has been the practice to kill or cast away anyone who is blind or crippled some way. Babies born that way have been thrown away for wild animals to devour. But wherever the Christian religion has been established, hospitals and homes have been built to take care of the handicapped people. What are ways in which each Christian family can help the handicapped though there are no such people in his neighborhood?

39

LUCIA GETS TOLD

Sparks of anger lit Ann's eyes as she climbed into the car when Mom came to bring her home from a birthday party at the Schramm's.

"Why, Ann," remarked Mom, "you look angry. What's the matter?"

"Well, I am. I'm just plain real mad. At Lucia."

"Now what's the matter with Lucia?"

"She thinks she's so—uppity, Mom. She comes to our party, and she gets out of that new car of theirs like she's stepping out of a golden chariot. She was wearing those silly white lace gloves that don't have any fingers in them. And she had her fingernails painted red—exactly to match their new red car.

"I could just see the other girls didn't like it one bit that Lucia had been invited to the party. But the Schramms were just trying to be fair. 'Course, none of us said anything about how we all felt, and we all *tried* to be nice to Lucia.

"Well, she kept those silly gloves on all the time. She

137

would hardly play any of the games the rest of us wanted to play because she didn't want to soil those lovely, lovely gloves. She was always spoiling the fun.

"And as if that wasn't enough, she starts telling us all that *her* ancestors came over on the *Mayflower,* and so her mother belongs to the D.A.R. She says the rest of us can't ever belong to the D.A.R. because *our* people are just descended from *immigrants.* Well, Myrtle said that didn't bother her any because she knew her grandparents were decent and good immigrants, and after all, we were *all* Americans.

"Pretty soon, most of the girls just up and left Lucia. They went to the barn loft to play. They knew they'd get rid of Lucia that way because Lucia wouldn't *ever* go into a *barn* with her lovely white gloves. So there I was, alone with her because I kept thinking of things we'd learned from the Bible—like, well being nice to people even when they persecute you [Rom. 12:14]. And you know what the Bible says about 'turning the other cheek' [Matt. 5:39]. Well, I was trying real hard, Mom, to turn the other cheek, but when Lucia started telling me all over again about what a handsome father *she* has and what a *scarecrow* Dad is, and what a lovely car they have and what a rattletrap we have, well, I just couldn't stand it any longer—and I just told Lucia off *good*.

"I told her I wouldn't trade my father for a thousand of hers, and I said we could have just as nice a car as theirs with the money Dad gives to the church and to people that are in need. And I told her that if they'd just give some money to the church instead of spending it on silly things like lace gloves without fingers, why, they might be doing some good, and I said—"

"Hmm," Mom interrupted, "I think you said enough." She slipped an arm around Ann's shoulders, and drove slowly as she added, "I don't really blame you at all for feeling the way you do. And I expect that if the same things had happened to me when I was a girl your age, I'd have done just what you did. But part of growing up is learning that it doesn't help any just to tell people off. It is much better if we learn that 'He that is slow to anger is better than the mighty; and he that ruleth his spirit than he that taketh a city' [Prov. 16:32].

"We've got to learn to bridle our tongues [James 3: 2-6], or our tongues will run away with us. The angrier we let ourselves get, the more our tongues will run away with us. That's when we say words that are unkind. And while we can later apologize for unkind words, we can never recall them.

"Being able to speak is something wonderful that only men can do. It is a gift God gave us that He didn't give the animals or birds or fish. Think how handicapped we would be if we couldn't speak to one another. Think how much good can be done by just speaking. Think how our pastor helps us each Sunday by just speaking to us, and how your teachers have helped you by speaking to you. Think how we can help others by speaking well of them, and by saying kind words to them."

"I wish I could *like* Lucia more," said Ann, "then I wouldn't want to tell her off."

"Well, now," said Mom with a big smile, "I know a girl who learned to like an old man that was grumpy and hard to like. And how did she begin to do it?"

"By praying for him. Like I can pray for Lucia," decided Ann.

MEMORY VERSE: *Do not return evil for evil or reviling for reviling; but on the contrary bless, for to this you have been called, that you may obtain a blessing.* I Peter 3:9 (RSV)

FAMILY DISCUSSION

1. Read Proverbs 13:3 and 21:23. Can you think of times when you kept your mouth shut when you felt like telling someone *plenty?* Were you glad afterwards that you did not "tell them off good"?

2. Read Matthew 5:38-43 to see what Christ wants us to do when people like Lucia say unkind things to us.

3. Think of some people outside your family who have used their gift of speech to help you.

40

PORCUPINE HEAD

"Well, if it is time for another story," said Dad, "I suppose I'd better put my story-thinking cap on."

"How about a story about Indians?" asked Paul.

Dad scratched his head. "Well, I know one about an Indian called Porcupine Head."

"Oh," said Mark, "this ought to be real good."

"Well, this Porcupine Head was a half-breed boy that lived out on the Fort Berthold Indian Reservation where Missionary Hall worked. Porcupine Head learned to be a cowboy, and when he grew up he had a ranch of his own on the Reservation. He used to drive cattle for many miles across the prairie to Minot and ship them to market from there

"Once when he had been to Minot and had taken a thousand dollars in cash from his bank, he put his wallet with all this money in it into his jacket pocket, and started driving home in his buggy. It got very hot that day, so Porcupine Head took his jacket off and laid it across the top of the buggy seat beside him. Somewhere along that trail, the wallet with the thousand dollars in it slipped out of the jacket pocket and into the grass. Porcupine Head didn't know what had happened until he got home late that night.

"Early the next morning, he started with fresh horses and searched the trail all the way back to Minot. He could not find his wallet. Homesteaders were flocking into that country at that time, so Porcupine Head was pretty sure some one of them had found his wallet. So

he returned to his bank and wanted to draw out another thousand dollars. But he had a banker friend who told him he ought to wait over till the next day, and maybe someone would return the wallet.

"Well, Porcupine Head was sure no one who found a thousand dollars in cash out on the prairies would return it, but to please his banker friend, he did stay overnight at Minot.

"The next morning when Porcupine Head came to the bank, his banker friend asked him to come into his office. There, standing beside the banker's desk was a homesteader in patched clothes, and that homesteader handed Porcupine Head his wallet.

"The man said to Porcupine Head, 'You count it over. I think all the money is there.'

PORCUPINE HEAD

"Porcupine Head could hardly believe his eyes. He counted the bills carefully and found that all his thousand dollars were there. Then he pulled out a hundred dollar bill and offered it to the homesteader. 'Take this,' he said, 'as a reward for bringing my money back to me.'

"But the homesteader would not take the hundred-dollar bill. 'The money is all yours,' he told Porcupine Head, 'I shouldn't have any of it for returning your own money to you.'

"Porcupine Head tried several times to get the homesteader to accept some money, but the homesteader always refused. Finally, Porcupine Head said, 'But I want to reward you some way.'

"Then the homesteader said, 'The best way you could reward me would be if you would become a Christian.'

"Porcupine Head was surprised at the homesteader's request. He could not quite understand it. He wasn't much interested in religion. He was mostly interested in making a lot of money. So he just shook hands with the homesteader and headed back for his ranch.

"But Porcupine Head could never forget that homesteader. He tried many times to find that homesteader and try again to reward him. But he was never able to find the homesteader. As the years passed, Porcupine Head found that he was never satisfied no matter how much money he made. And he kept remembering how contented and joyful looking that poor homesteader had been, and how honest and decent the man had been. He kept remembering, too, how that homesteader had asked him to become a Christian.

"Finally, Porcupine Head started going to church, and he did become a Christian."

"Did the homesteader ever find out that Porcupine Head became a Christian?" Ann asked.

"No," replied Dad, "I'm sure the homesteader never learned that because of his humble testimony those few minutes he was with Porcupine Head, that one day Porcupine Head was to become a Christian. You see, each of us little knows how much we may be able to help people —or hurt them—by what we do and say, any day. That homesteader was no important person, and we may think that we aren't important and so what *we* do and say isn't important. But, for all we know, someone we least expect may be brought closer—or farther—from Christ, by what *we* do and say."

"That homesteader," said Mom, "will have his reward in heaven. For 'whosoever therefore shall confess me before men, him will I confess also before my Father which is in heaven'" (Matt. 10:32).

MEMORY VERSE: *Whosoever therefore shall confess me before men, him will I confess also before my Father which is in heaven.* Matthew 10:32

FAMILY DISCUSSION

1. What are ways in which children can confess Christ before men by what they *do?*

2. If we could have met this homesteader in patched clothes, would we have considered him an important person or a leading Christian? (Read Matthew 19:23-30). In God's sight, how do you think this humble homesteader will stand? One of the "first [that] shall be last" or one of the "last [that] shall be first"?

3. What should we do if we find something that is not ours? If we say, "Finders, keepers," what Commandment are we breaking?

41

ANN BRINGS A NEW IDEA

After a week's visit at the Nichols home in Wood-bridge, Ann had much to tell. "It was fun to live in town. We went to the grocery store at least once every day because whenever Mrs. Nichols needed something she'd just send Janie and me to get it. It's not like the way we do it—all our shopping in one trip each week. We went to the post office to get the mail instead of running down to the mail box." Thus, on and on, Ann reported her exciting week in the little town of Wood-bridge.

"I'm glad you had such a nice time," said Mom. "Some time when Janie invites you again, you may go for another visit. And we'll want Janie to come out here for a week."

"You know," remarked Ann, "Janie's family had something, oh, sort of nice and special in their house—something that maybe we could fix up, too."

"What was that?"

"They called it their 'worship center.' It sort of reminded you of an altar. It was really just a table with a

145

Bible lying on it, and a big picture of Christ hanging over it. They had two big candles in copper holders on either side of the Bible. After they had read from their Bible in the evening, they would light the candles while they talked about what they had read. Then they would pray, and they would sit there and sing a few hymns in the candlelight. Seemed almost like being in church."

"Would you like to have a worship center like that in our house?" Mom asked.

"Oh, yes," said Ann. Melissa, too, nodded her head in agreement.

That evening as the Johnson family gathered in the living room, Dad and the boys were surprised at what they saw. Above the small walnut bookcase there now hung the family's favorite picture of Christ. Dad's big Bible lay open on top of the bookcase, and behind it stood the wooden cross that Grandfather Johnson had carved for the little sodhouse church that had stood many years before where the white frame Pleasant Valley Church now stood. On either side of the Bible and the cross there gleamed tall white candles set in Grandmother Johnson's brass candlesticks.

So, after they had read together from their Bibles, Ann and Melissa each lit a candle after turning out all the lights. Then in the glow of the candles, the Johnsons said their Bible verses together, talked and prayed and sang together, and when they had finished, Paul whispered happily, "It's like we have a church in our house!"

"Yes," said Dad, "the candles burning beside the cross do remind us of an altar, but of course, it isn't the candles or the cross that makes the 'church in our house' [Rom. 16:5; I Cor. 16:19; Philem. 2]—it is the presence

146

A NEW IDEA

of Christ here with us, for He promised that 'where two or three are gathered together in my name, there am I in the midst of them'" (Matt. 18:20).

MEMORY VERSE: *For where two or three are gathered in my name, there am I in the midst of them.* Matthew 18:20 (RSV)

FAMILY DISCUSSION

1. What *is* the church? (Romans 12:5; I Corinthians 12:27)

2. Must we have an altar or a place for worship in order to be able to worship God? Where did Jacob, Abraham and Moses worship? Where did the shepherds worship the baby Jesus?

3. While it is possible to worship God though we have no church building, do you think we would worship God as regularly if we did not have a church to which to go each Sunday? (Psalm 122:1; Hebrews 10:25)

4. Did Jesus have the church-going habit? (Matthew 12:9; Mark 1:21; Luke 4:16)

42

SILENT SERMONS IN CHURCH

Melissa looked at the carved letters on the front of the pulpit as though she had never seen them before. "J, H, S," she spelled out to herself. "Now what could they mean?"

Dad would surely know. So, as soon as the Johnsons had assembled in their car to go home, Melissa popped her question. "Dad, what do those letters on the pulpit mean?"

"Letters on the pulpit?" puzzled her father. "I'm not sure what you mean."

"Oh, you know—those things carved right on the front of the pulpit. They look like J, H, S."

"Oh, yes. Those are letters. We call them the sacred monogram. They are a sort of symbol that stands for Jesus Christ, our Savior."

"Symbol? What's a symbol?"

"Well, if we saw a red flag in the road ahead of us now, what could that red flag mean?"

"Danger ahead."

"Exactly. The red flag, then, is a *symbol* of danger

148

ahead. And those carved letters on our church pulpit are a symbol for Christ. The cross on our altar is a symbol, too, of Christ having died on the cross for our sins.

"In our church, Melissa, those happen to be the only symbols there are. But when you visit some other churches, especially some large ones, you may see many different symbols. Oh, you would see them in stained glass windows. On doors. On the altar or the pulpit or baptismal font. You might see doves and triangles, stars and circles, candlesticks, flames, all sorts of crosses—and each one would stand for something because it's a church symbol."

"How come?" asked Mark.

"Well, these church symbols got started way back in the early days of the Christian church when the Christians were persecuted by the Romans. One of the first symbols for Jesus Christ was a fish. A woman in Rome might wear a shell tied to a string around her neck, and there would be a fish painted on the shell to show that she was a follower of Christ. That way, other Christians just passing her on the street, would know that she was another Christian."

"But how did they come to use a *fish* as a symbol for Christ?" asked Mark.

"It happens that the first letters of the Greek words that are used to describe Jesus as God's Son and our Savior spelled the word for 'fish.' So, either the word or the picture of a fish became a secret password or sign among the Christians. Many of the graves in the Catacombs have a fish carved on them to show that these are the graves of Christians. That is how it happens that in some Christian churches today, you find fish symbols and dozens of other symbols that Christians made use of especially during the first centuries after Christ was here on earth."

"Say," Ann said, "I saw some symbols in Janie's church, and I wondered what they were for. There was a lamb in the window near where we sat."

"And what do you suppose the lamb could be a symbol of?"

"Oh, I know," said Stephen. "The lamb must stand for Jesus because He is the Lamb that takes away the sin of the world" (John 1:29).

"That's right. And likewise, you'll find every symbol has a hidden meaning. They don't *say* anything—and yet, when we understand what each symbol means, each one preaches a little sermon to us. I think one of the biggest sermons they all preach together is that *we* can be so thankful that we live in a country where we are *free* to be Christians, and we don't have to wear secret signs or hide from anyone because we are Christians."

MEMORY VERSE: *Behold the Lamb of God, who takes away the sin of the world!* John 1:29 (RSV)

FAMILY DISCUSSION

1. Think of the different symbols you have seen in churches. What do they mean?

2. Why do so many churches use candles? (They are usually a symbol of "The Light of the World.")

3. Various churches differ a great deal in their use of church symbols. But there is one symbol that is used in all Christian churches, no matter what the denomination may be. It has been under this greatest of all Christian church symbols that Christians have gone forth in the name of the Lord. What is this sign? (The cross.)

150

43

A LESSON FOR ANN

The sun shone brightly, promising a beautiful day for the parade at Woodbridge. Ann loved parades—any kind —and this one was to be a special Kiddie Parade. The children of Woodbridge were to dress in costumes. The girls would be pushing decorated doll buggies. The boys would have decorated bicycles, coaster wagons and pedal cars. Some would lead their pets, and the pets would have costumes, too!

Now Mom was calling. "Ann, have you started cleaning the eggs? We must have them all ready to take with us when we go to Woodbridge."

To go down to the basement on a sunshiny day and clean and pack eggs just did not appeal to Ann one whit. She would be glad when Melissa was old enough to take *her* turn at the egg chores.

"Yes, Mom," Ann answered now. "I'll get at the eggs soon."

There was plenty of time to do the egg chores, Ann decided, after a glance at her bedroom clock. It would be three hours before they would leave for Woodbridge.

151

She decided she would read one chapter in her new book before she went down to the egg chores.

The new book of adventure proved especially interesting. Ann read two chapters before she took another look at the clock. Then she scurried to the basement. She had been working there only a short time when Mom called, "Time to get dressed for town, Ann!"

"But I haven't finished with the eggs yet," answered Ann, alarmed. She could see there were at least twice as many eggs left to clean and pack.

Mom looked down the basement. "Why, Ann! Are you still packing eggs? Why, whatever has taken you so long this time?"

Ann flushed. "Oh, I just got started a little while ago."

Mom threw up her hands. "The parade starts in just an hour. The rest of us have finished our work, and we have begun to get dressed. But we can't go until these eggs are ready to go with us."

Ann hurried. But hurrying and packing eggs did not go well together. She squeezed one thin-shelled egg too hard and so it cracked and spilled over her hand and into the packing crate. She dropped another egg to the floor and it splattered over her shoes and socks. She was in tears when Mark and Stephen, in their dress-up clothes, bounded down to help her.

Evidently, Mom had cautioned the boys not to scold Ann for being so pokey about her job, but they scolded her plenty with their eyes. When they had finished, Ann jumped up to wash and change clothes while Stephen and Mark impatiently carried the egg cases out to the car trunk.

They brought the eggs to the creamery in their own

152

little village, then drove on to Woodbridge. When they reached the main street of Woodbridge, they spied only a few decorated bicycles and children showing off gay costumes. The parade, they learned, had just ended.

"Too late, of course," grumbled Mark. "All because Ann didn't tend to her egg business on time."

Ann burst into tears. It was bad enough to miss the Kiddie Parade without being scolded by Mark. But worst of all was to realize that because she had failed in her responsibility, the whole family had missed the fun.

"We got *our* work done on time," said Mark. "It isn't fair that we should all miss the parade."

"No," replied Mom, "it isn't fair. But that's the way things work out. When one person in the family fails to do his part, things just go wrong for the whole family. 'For none of us liveth to himself'" (Rom. 14:7).

MEMORY VERSE: *Whatever your task, work heartily, as serving the Lord and not men.* Colossians 3:23 (RSV)

FAMILY DISCUSSION

1. Ann did not enjoy her egg cleaning and packing chores. Is that the way it is with most of us—that we have some chores or jobs to do that we may not *enjoy* doing? What does Colossians 3:23 say about our work?

2. In our house, what are the daily responsibilities that each one of us has?

3. Are some of us able to take more responsibilities?

4. In a nation-wide survey some years ago, it was found that there is one thing that employers always look for in the man or woman, the boy or girl, they want to hire for a job. That one thing is *responsibility*. How do we learn *responsibility?*

44

PAUL AND THE ECHO

Paul stood in the empty silo, surprised to find that his red hen had found her way there. "Why, here you are!" he shouted gleefully at his pet.

"Why, here you are!" echoed back at him from the high, empty silo.

Paul was astonished. "Say!" he exclaimed.

"Say!" came back the echo.

Here was a new game. For several minutes, Paul had fun shouting into the silo, and listening to the echo of whatever he had shouted. Sometimes the echo was not clear, but always he could hear his voice repeated.

He bounded to the house to tell Mom and Dad of his discovery. He decided he would bring Beth and Melissa back with him to play the echo game.

"Why, everything I say comes right back to me," Paul explained to his parents. "And it's fun."

"Yes," said Dad, "that's sort of like a game they play in a faraway country. There they have something they call a boomerang—they throw this boomerang into the

154

air, and what do you suppose, it comes right back to the person who threw it!"

"A boomerang would be fun," said Paul, "if I just had a boomerang. But I can play in the silo, and the silo will throw back to me what I say. If I sing, it sings back to me. If I growl grumpy it comes back grumpy to me."

"It's not just in the silo that you can play the echo game," said Mom. "We all play the echo game every day because when we say happy things to other people, they are pretty sure to say happy things back to us. When we are cross to other people, other people may get cross right back at us. For 'whatsoever a man soweth, that shall he also reap'" (Gal. 6:7).

MEMORY VERSE: *Behold, I am coming soon, bringing my recompense to repay everyone for what he has done.* Revelation 22:12 (RSV)

FAMILY DISCUSSION

1. Think of some of the happiest people you know. When you are with them, do they make you happy? Are they reaping what they "sow"?

2. Why is a grumpy voice like a boomerang? Will it hurt others, too? If we use such a voice, will it come back and hurt us, too?

3. When we do or say things to other people, is it the same as saying and doing them to Jesus? (Matthew 25:40)

45

UP IN THE TREE HOUSE

Mark and Ann scrambled up the old tree to the tree house they had built from lumber scraps Dad had given them. Once inside the treehouse, Mark quickly spied the pile of comic books in one corner. "Say," he exclaimed, "comic books! Where did you get them? You know Mom says we aren't to buy any unless she—"

"Oh, I know," countered Ann, smugly. "I didn't buy them at all. The Schramm twins gave them all to me."

For the next minutes, neither Ann nor Mark said much as they busily scanned the brightly colored covers of the books. "Boy, talk about exciting," said Mark after he had settled down with one, "why here it tells how these crooks stole a car that was locked—it has pictures to show just how they got inside that locked car. Why, *I* could get into a locked car that way!"

"But you wouldn't want to steal a car!"

"Of course not."

"Lookit here, Mark. Here's this girl. She's wearing—well, it looks like some sort of bathing suit. But she's riding a horse, mind you. She is supposed to be way out in some wild mountains. Kind of silly, don't you think, a girl like that, out trailing outlaws?"

"Yes, silly," agreed Mark. Then he riffled through the pile to see what else there might be of special interest. For about an hour, brother and sister read quietly until they heard Mom calling them to the noon meal.

That evening as the Johnsons gathered in the living room, Mark and Ann were very surprised to see a collection of their comic books lying on the end table beside Dad's chair. Ann put her hand to her mouth. She had not intended that the comic books should ever get into the house. Those comic books were certainly not the kind that Mom and Dad would ever buy for them!

No one said anything about the comic books. But Mark and Ann blushed as each settled down with a Bible. Twice, Ann had to be prompted on which verse it was her turn to read because all she could think of was, "How did those comics get in here? What will Mom and Dad say now?"

When the family had finished with the Bible chapter, Dad said, without looking at anyone in particular, "Melissa found these comic books up in the tree house. She brought them to Mother and wanted Mother to read them to her. Mother decided we'd wait with the comic book reading until our family hour and see if there were others in the family who would like to have her read to them from these comic books."

Dad handed the comic books to Mom. Slowly, Mom held each comic book up for all to see.

Silence filled the room as Dad and Mom waited for one of the children to select a comic book for Mom to read. Ann and Mark blushed furiously.

"Well," said Mom, at last, "I guess nobody here wants me to read these comic books. And that suits me fine because I wouldn't enjoy any of these myself."

"No," observed Dad, "somehow comic books just don't seem to fit for family reading." Then he looked at Mark and Ann kindly. "There are all sorts of comic books. Some we might say are perfectly harmless. Some tell excellent stories. But we know, too, that hundreds of them are poor reading for children. The police records show that many boys and girls have gotten into trouble because they tried to do what they had read about how to do in comic books. There are many children in reform schools today, and grownups serving prison terms, because they learned how to do wrong from comic books.

"Now, I can readily see why you might like a comic book. All of us like to look at pictures. For that reason there are many picture magazines published. It is easier to look at pictures than to read. The pictures in comic books are like the pictures in the Funny Papers, but it is hard on our eyes to look at that kind of poorly printed and badly colored pictures, and to read the kind of print that goes with such pictures.

"I know that some of the best stories in our literature have been put in comic books, but these picture stories in comic books can never tell the story as well as they were told the way the master writer first wrote them.

"Some of these comic books have stories about stealing and murdering. Our Bible has stories in it about stealing and murdering, too. But when you read about killing and stealing in the Bible, it is always made plain to you that killing and stealing are sins, and not something you'd want to try yourself.

158

THE TREE HOUSE

"Mother and I want you children to enjoy reading, and we are glad that you like to read. But we want you to enjoy the kind of books you are not ashamed to read right in our living room with the rest of us."

Then Dad opened his Bible to Philippians 4:8 and he read to his family:

"Finally, brethren, whatsoever things are true, whatsoever things are honest, whatsoever things are just, whatsoever things are pure, whatsoever things are lovely, whatsoever things are of good report; if there be any virtue, and if there be any praise, think on these things."

Mom nodded her head, "Yes, let's think of that verse when we choose our books for reading. The kind of books we read help make us the kind of men and women we become."

Later, as they prayed and sang together in the candlelight, Ann felt better. She knew that in the morning, she would clean house up in the tree house, and the rest of those comic books would be tossed into the trash burner.

MEMORY VERSE: *Blessed are the pure in heart: for they shall see God.* Matthew 5:8

FAMILY DISCUSSION

1. Let each one in the family who is old enough to read tell about his or her favorite book. Why is it a favorite book?
2. What makes a good book?
3. Think of some of the books that may have been written long ago, and have been enjoyed by young and old people ever since. (Read such books together, as a family, and you can develop a reading taste not tempted by comic books.)

46

SLIGHTLY SOILED, MARKED DOWN

Several men, laughing heartily, stood about the show-room of the farm implement store in Woodbridge. Stephen and his father had joined the group when they recognized two of their own neighbors. One of them was Mr. Ronaldson, a member of their own church.

"Quite a story, quite a story," chuckled one of the strangers. "I can tell you one just as good," said another stranger. Then he told a dirty story that made the men roar with laughter again.

Stephen, embarrassed, looked at his father. Dad was the only man who was not laughing.

Silently now, he took Stephen by the arm and they walked out of the store.

As they got into their car to go home, Stephen said, "Dad, I never thought that Mr. Ronaldson would laugh at a dirty story like that. Why, he goes to our church!"

"Yes," said Dad, sadly, "he goes to our church." For a few moments, he was silent. Then he added, "Remember that sign in the store where we bought those shirts at bargain prices because they had become soiled?"

160

SLIGHTLY SOILED

"Sure. You mean that sign that said "slightly soiled. Marked down'?"

"That's it. I can imagine that is the way you feel about Mr. Ronaldson now—that he's slightly soiled and marked down in your estimation."

"You're right, Dad." Stephen's eyes were serious. There was hurt in them, too. He had always admired Mr. Ronaldson. Mr. Ronaldson was a pleasant man, one of the most successful farmers in the Pleasant Valley neighborhood, and he always had a cheerful greeting for everyone.

"We'll hope and pray," said Dad, "that our friend Ronaldson will learn to 'Abhor that which is evil; cleave to that which is good'" (Rom. 12:9).

Dad laid a hand on Stephen's arm. "Next year, you'll be going to high school, Son. You'll be mixing with a lot of different kinds of boys. Some of them are going to have a lot of smutty stories to tell."

"I'll remember, Dad," Stephen promised, "to try not to get slightly soiled and marked down."

MEMORY VERSE: *Be not overcome of evil, but overcome evil with good.* Romans 12:21

FAMILY DISCUSSION

1. Read I Thessalonians 5:22. We'll imagine that you play with friends who are known to do pranks that are sometimes not kind, even destructive. You do not join with them in such pranks. Do you think that some folks might think—because you are with such children—that you are "slightly soiled, marked down"?

2. Is there a danger that if you keep on playing with friends

that like to do harmful pranks that you may weaken and take part in such pranks?

3. Notice that the Bible points out that it is not enough just to stay away from evil, but that we must also put good in the place of evil. If you have a bad habit you want to get rid of, what then should you put in its place? If you play with children who are inclined to do naughty tricks, what should you then try to do for them?

4. God hates sin, but He loves the sinner. While we are to "abhor evil," how should we feel toward those who may do evil or things that we know are not right? (Romans 12:9)

5. What is our reward for turning from evil, and doing good? (I Peter 3:11-12)

47

A LETTER FROM JOSEFA

On Saturday morning, Mark bounded up the road from the mail box, excitedly waving the day's mail and shouting, "A letter from Josefa!"

Within a few minutes, he was in the kitchen and Mom was reading the letter to the children:

"Dear Family:

"I am so happy because I get letter from my good teacher, Pastor Peterson, and he tell me you let me have your name Johnson because I am your son in Lord Jesus. This give me so great joy for now I have both a good name and a family that will have me.

"I go from this Bible school now. I go back to the hills of my people to bring them the Gospel. I help the missionary there to teach the Bible stories to children. I will talk to the young men of my tribe, and to the old ones, and tell them about Jesus so they may be free like I am. Now they are bound by devil worship, and they are afraid of demons and evil spirits. I want them to have the so great joy I have in my heart because I am Christian.

"I have never felt lonely since Pastor Peterson tell me about my family in America that I never see. He tell me

163

you send money to Bible school to help me even though you never knew me, but because you love Jesus and want to help Malagasy boy to love Jesus, too.

"Your letters I get make me so happy. You lift up my heart.

"How I would like to see my Johnson family. Some day perhaps a Johnson brother or sister come here to help with our mission. Then I see you, and tell you more how so great help you are to me.

"Please write many times to me.

> "Your son and brother in Jesus,
> "JOSEFA JOHNSON"

With the letter was another picture of Josefa. Ann was quick to notice that in this picture he was wearing *decent* clothes. Josefa had been photographed with his classmates at the Bible school.

Mom's eyes brimmed with joyous tears when Dad came in to see what was in the mail. She handed him Josefa's letter, saying, "Here is a letter from our Malagasy son!"

MEMORY VERSE: *There is neither Jew nor Greek, there is neither bond nor free, there is neither male nor female: for ye are all one in Christ Jesus.* Galatians 3:28

FAMILY DISCUSSION

1. Read Ecclesiastes 11:1. How does this apply to the Johnsons?

2. For four years, the Johnsons have been sending money to the Bible school to help Josefa. Which, do you think, would have given them the greatest happiness, saving this money to spend on themselves, or giving it to Josefa's needs? Of what Bible verse that you have memorized does this remind you? (Acts 20:35)

48

GRANDPA HAGLUND AT
HAPPY ACRES

"Hi," said little Beth to Mr. Haglund as she climbed into her high chair just across the table from the old man.

Mr. Haglund looked at Beth, but he said nothing.

So Beth blinked her eyes at him, smiled her widest smile and said, "We like me. Don't you like me, too?"

Mr. Haglund could not keep from smiling at that. He said, "Ya. I like you. I had a little girl like you once. I called her *Tulla* because she had curly hair."

"Me curly hair, too. Me, *Tulla*, too?"

"Ya," said the old man. "You be a *Tulla*, too!"

He said little more during the meal, but he did manage to smile again, this time at Ann when she asked him politely if there wasn't something she could pass him.

When he stood up from the table, he turned to Mom and he bowed stiffly to her, saying, "A thousand thanks for the supper. It was good."

Mr. Haglund had both smiled and thanked! Ann wanted

to jump up and down for joy. But she stood very quietly, then began to help Mom clear the table.

An hour later, the old man was ready to leave for the Rest Home. But this time when he reached the door, he turned around. He took off his old black hat. He turned it around in his hands.

Ann could see there was something he was trying hard to tell. He cleared his throat and rumbled "Harrumph!" Then, with both hands pressed against his hat, he said to Mom, "You have been good to me. Thank you for the cards you send me. And for the slippers. I am an old man. I have no money. You have been good to me when you knew I could never do anything in return."

Ann saw Mr. Haglund's lips trembling as though he wanted to cry. "My wife—she was a good woman. Like you. She believed in the Bible, too. You and your man here—you believe in the Bible. That is why you have been so good to me. Is it not so?"

Mom's eyes were dewy as she nodded. "Yes, it is so. 'For the love of Christ constrains us' " (II Cor. 5:14).

There was a big tear in one of Mr. Haglund's squinty eyes as he said, "This morning I take from my trunk my wife's Bible. Now I read it. I want to believe in Jesus, too. I have seen Jesus in you people."

The grumpiness would all go away, Ann knew. Already there was a new gentleness in the old man.

As he turned to go out the door, he smiled right into Ann's face and said, "Good night, Girlie."

His voice was tender. Ann felt almost as though he had patted her shoulder.

He would be coming back to Happy Acres many times,

GRANDPA HAGLUND

she knew. With Jesus in his heart, he would be another grandfather for the Johnsons!

MEMORY VERSE: *For the love of Christ controls us, because we are convinced that one has died for all; therefore all have died. And He died for all, that those who live might live no longer for themselves but for him who for their sake died and was raised.* II Corinthians 5:14-15 (RSV)